THE UNSEEN WORLD

NEW YORK 1962

The
Rockefeller
Institute
1901

PRO·BONO·HUMANI·GENERIS

THE

BY RENÉ DUBOS

UNSEEN

THE ROCKEFELLER INSTITUTE PRESS

WORLD

in association with OXFORD UNIVERSITY PRESS

To those who search

for the glow of life

in the unseen world

René Dubos

Contents

Foreword

THE LECTURES which are retold in this book have a distinguished ancestry.

While immortal Michael Faraday was a young apprentice to a London bookseller, he was taken to hear Sir Humphrey Davy lecture in the House of the Royal Institution of Great Britain. Faraday grasped these lectures so readily and reported them so well that Davy was persuaded to employ the boy as his assistant.

When Faraday was made Director of the Laboratory of the Royal Institution in 1825, it was natural that he should with gratitude recall Davy's lectures. Accordingly, one of his first acts as Director was to start a course of lectures for children delivered at Christmas time. It was his object "to interest the young in the principles of science in an entertaining way rather than merely to amuse them with sensational and topical oddments of scientific information or to instruct them in textbook knowledge as in a schoolroom."

Faraday himself gave the second *Christmas Course of Lectures Adapted to a Juvenile Auditory* in 1827. Because they were eagerly attended and enthusiastically applauded, Faraday was encouraged to lecture again in 1829 when he spoke on electricity and his electrical experiments.

As is characteristic of most pioneers of science, Faraday was an inspiring teacher: enthusiastic in the telling of his hardly discovered knowledge, lucid, deeply interested in students; as an experimental lecturer, he was supreme. And so he gladly gave nineteen of the Christmas Lectures until his retirement in 1861. Now, after 130 years, the custom he started still continues as one of the significant functions of the Royal Institution.

Those annual lectures have had a far-reaching influence. They have attracted hundreds of young men and women to careers in science. They have inspired men of science to speak with patience and humility to those who may be their successors. Because scientific phenomena and principles have been described in simple language, the lectures have revealed the spirit of science to people of all ages. And now they have set the pattern for another series of which this volume is the first.

The Rockefeller Institute was devoted to medical research from the time it was founded in 1901 until 1955. In the latter year its scope was extended to include a School of Graduate Studies comprising many fields of science and the humanities as well.

As we assumed our teaching functions, Professor Alfred Mirsky recalled the Royal Institution Christmas Lectures. He suggested that a graduate university should be concerned with high school students because some high school students will ultimately become graduate students of science if someone arouses their interest in science. Accordingly, The Rockefeller Institute Christmas Lectures were begun in 1959 with the financial assistance of the National Science Foundation.

If the early Christmas Lectures of the Royal Institution had not been delivered by a scientist who had Faraday's remarkable talents, it is doubtful that the lectures would have been continued. The Rockefeller Institute faced a similar challenge: who could give the first series so that more would be desired in succeeding years? Our choice of René Dubos was obvious.

By his brilliant research, Professor Dubos has contributed greatly to the advancement of the sciences of life. But his scientific horizons stretch far beyond the reach of his own laboratories. Through his lucid prose and fluent exposition, he has led countless others toward those far horizons. As Tyndall said of Faraday, Dubos "is apt to teach."

In the final chapter of this book, Professor Dubos tells of the questions and discussions which followed each of his lectures. Those who were privileged to hear the conversations will long remember them as deeply moving experiences. The questions revealed eager, imaginative, perceptive minds seeking truth and understanding. The youthful listeners properly desired knowledge about things, but they wisely wished also to know how that knowledge had been gained and how it may grow.

As the deafening applause that followed the last lecture was finally arrested, I thought of Faraday and his students who preceeded Dubos and the students gathered about him. I was thus reminded that we are indebted to our predecessors for the knowledge which enables us to go beyond the limits of their knowledge, and that we find our fulfillment in our successors.

DETLEV W. BRONK

CHAPTER ONE

Microscopic Cells and Giant Crystals

I AM A MICROBIOLOGIST, and most of my professional life has been spent studying the behavior of microbes found in the earth and in the air, or causing disease in animals and human beings. Enlightened men appreciate the social services rendered by my profession, but I realize that there are few who find in it any human significance beyond technical achievements. Microbiology, like other sciences, is usually regarded as having no relevance to the deep preoccupations of the man of flesh and bone.

Yet, never in my professional life do I find myself far removed from the man of flesh and bone. It is not only because microbes are ubiquitous in our environment and therefore must be studied for the sake of human welfare. Far more important in my opinion is the fact that microbes exhibit profound resemblances to man. They resemble him in their physical makeup, in their chemical composition and activities, and in their responses to various stimuli. They also display associations among themselves and with other living things which suggest illuminating analogies with human societies. By revealing

1

the deep-seated unity that prevails through all the manifestations of life, microbiology has added an important stone to the structure of philosophical thought.

I shall write of microbiology not only in its technical aspects, but also in its relevance to problems of life in general and of human life in particular. First, however, I must make a few remarks concerning large social and human aspects of scientific life that microbiologists share with other natural scientists.

Modern societies may not be wiser than those of the past, but it is obvious that they have grown materially richer by learning to use science for the control and exploitation of nature. Scientists naturally take pride in the fact that their achievements now give them such a large social role. In the mind of many of them, however, the creation of wealth and of power ranks rather low among the forces that account for their dedication to scientific work. Most scientists have elected science as a profession not because it leads to practical ends, but rather because it is interesting for its own sake. They sense, furthermore, that science has become the lifeblood of modern culture. In addition to being a source of power and of material wealth, science enlarges human vision and thus enriches all esthetic and ethical values. By helping to define the place of man in the order of things, it deeply influences philosophical and even religious thought. Today, more than ever, science should be regarded as "natural philosophy."

Laymen tend to believe that science is an esoteric pursuit. In truth, however, great universities and research institutes have not had in the past a monopoly on significant scientific work, and I am convinced that discoveries will continue to be made outside of academic walls in the future. The Christmas lectures that have been delivered at the Royal Institution since the beginning of the 19th century teach an interesting and important lesson in this regard. One of the most successful series of lectures was presented in 1848 by Michael Faraday under the title "The Chemical History of a Candle." On that occasion, Faraday illustrated how one can learn many important facts of chemistry and physics from observations made on a simple wax candle, and on the way it burns. In 1889 another series of popular lectures was given by C. V. Boys on the subject "Soap Bubbles and the Forces which Mould Them." Like Faraday, Boys showed that profound laws of nature can be derived from experiments carried on with simple materials and equipment — in this case with ordinary soap bubbles. It might be useful to take notice here of statements made by Academician N. Semenov at the 22nd Congress of the Communist Party in 1961. According to him, over one million Russian citizens now belong to the Society for the Dissemination of Knowledge and it is expected that more and more of them will devote some of their leisure time to creative participation in the advancement of science.

History shows, in fact, that some of the most interesting natural phenomena have been discovered by men who were not professional scientists, but were simple amateurs working with tools and techniques no more complicated than those which anyone can own and operate in his own home. In passing, it is worth noting that the word *amateur* etymologically means "one who loves." Almost any intelligent and industrious person can become a true scientist, if he is an amateur in the original sense of the word and really loves what he does. One of the best illustrations of this truth is provided by the story of Antony van Leeuwenhoek, the founder of the science of microbiology. Leeuwenhoek is known as one of the immortals of science, and yet he was not a professional scientist, but rather a true "amateur" if there ever was one.

L E E U W E N H O E K lived from 1632–1723 in the small town of Delft, Holland, where he followed the profession of draper and also acted as surveyor and alderman. It is relatively easy for us to imagine the environment in which he lived because several beautiful paintings of Delft were made at that time. In fact, the most famous of these paintings is by the Dutch artist Vermeer, who was born in Delft the same year as Leeuwenhoek and who probably knew him. Delft was then a charming small town, a prosperous business center and the seat of a celebrated university, but far removed, nevertheless, from the hustle and bustle of the world. Try to imagine the life of the small merchant, Antony van Leeuwenhoek, in the peaceful atmosphere evoked by Vermeer's painting. He had received very little schooling, spoke and wrote an ungrammatical Dutch, and his contacts with men of learning were at first very infrequent. At work in his neat but humble home, his appearance and behavior were very different from the popular image of the modern professional scientist handling mysterious equipment in a mechanized laboratory. Yet it is in the simple surroundings of this quaint Dutch home that Leeuwenhoek made the fundamental discoveries which established him as one of the founders of microscopy and the father of microbiology.

Leeuwenhoek, like many of his contemporaries, had made a hobby of grinding lenses and looking through them at all sorts of objects — much as many persons today wire hi-fi sets, build home telescopes, or collect beetles. Totally untrained, and working alone, he developed nevertheless an extraordinary skill in the art of lens grinding which probably has never been excelled. Within the confines of his small workroom, he turned out hundreds of tiny lenses that he mounted between two thin sheets of silver or brass with

Vermeer painted these two views of Delft around 1658. The house (right) is probably very like the one in which Leeuwenhoek lived. The water and mud of the canal (left) were among the many materials in which he discovered microbial life, and recognized its abundance and variety.

small openings masking all but the central area of the lens. By this simple procedure he obtained the sharpness of image that the modern photographer obtains by stopping down his camera lens. It is a truly remarkable fact that even though his microscopes were made of a single lens their optical quality was such that he could obtain magnifications ranging from 40 to 275 diameters. In general, the minute objects to be observed were impaled before the lens on needle points adjustable with thumbscrews both for height and for distance. In addition, some of his microscopes were specially designed to hold minute glass vials or capillary tubes so that he could bring liquids within extremely short focal ranges.

It is a wonder indeed that with such primitive instruments Leeuwenhoek could see the many details that he described. The first and most important reason for his success certainly was the loving

5

care that he applied to the making and handling of his tools. To give an idea of his technical skill and attention to details, I cannot do better than quote from the August 2, 1701 letter by which he bequeathed some of his equipment to the Royal Society in London: "I have a very little Cabinet, lacquered black and gilded, that comprehendeth within it five little drawers, wherein lie inclosed 13 long and square little tin cases, which I have covered over with black leather; and in each of these little cases lie two ground magnifying-glasses (making 26 in all), every one of them ground by myself, and mounted in silver, and furthermore set in silver, almost all of them in silver that I extracted from the ore, and separated from the gold wherewith it was charged; and therewithal is writ down what object standeth before each little glass."

Leeuwenhoek must have been endowed with exceptional eye-

Antony van Leeuwenhoek (about 54 years of age); steel engraving from a portrait by J. Verkolje in the Amsterdam Rijksmuseum.

6

In the drawing (at the left), the artist has represented the manner in which Leeuwenhoek used his homemade single lens microscope. Figure 1 (below) shows the whole instrument from the back, ready for use; Figure 4 is a diagrammatic longitudinal section.

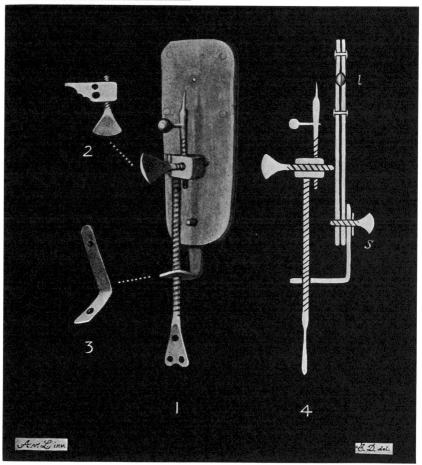

sight and a great power of observation; moreover he probably developed ingenious technical procedures such as dark-field illumination. I say "probably" because he was very secretive about his techniques and refused to reveal them either in conversation or in writing, even to his closest friends. Since he was so secretive about his methods and left no record of them, one may ask how we know so much about his discoveries? For this we are indebted to one of Delft's citizens, the famous Dutch physician Regnier de Graaf, who was interested in Leeuwenhoek's findings because of his own anatomical work and who obtained his permission to send a description of them to the Royal Society of London in 1673. The Fellows of the Royal Society were so much intrigued that they made Leeuwenhoek one of their corresponding members. This gave rise to a 50-year correspondence during which Leeuwenhoek wrote 375 letters to the Royal Society describing in great detail, if not his techniques, at least the wonders that he saw through his microscopes.

Leeuwenhoek's letters were written in colloquial Dutch, but their naive conversational style was so picturesque and his reports so objective that even today there is no doubt concerning the nature of the objects that he described. And these objects were drawn from a large part of biology—including insect wings, human spermatozoa, blood vessels, and the microbial life in water. His curiosity was unbounded, and he looked with wonder and excitement on almost any object revealed by his lenses. One of his most startling observations, which constitutes the very beginning of the science of bacteriology, was made when he examined material that he had taken from between his teeth and had resuspended in rain water or saliva. In two letters to the Royal Society, one in 1683 and the other in 1692, he reported seeing minute bodies that we can now identify as bacteria. The letters were illustrated with drawings representing the various kinds of "animalcules" that he described.

The significance of the drawings on pages 9 and 11 showing the very first bacteria seen by man becomes clear when it is realized that the observer lived 250 years ago and that his tool was a simple one-lens microscope built with his own hands!

8

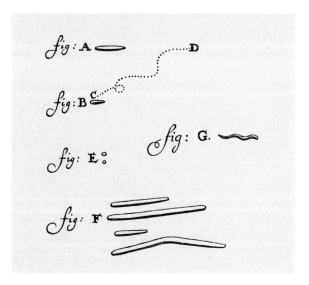

LEEUWENHOEK'S FIGURES OF BACTERIA FROM THE HUMAN MOUTH

FIGURE A, *a motile* Bacillus.
FIGURE B, Selenomonas sputigena.   *C . . . . D, the path of its motion.*
FIGURE E, *Micrococci.*
FIGURE F, Leptothrix buccalis.
FIGURE G, *A spirochæte — probably* "Spirochaeta buccalis," *the largest
     form found in this situation.*

[FROM LEEUWENHOEK'S LETTER OF SEPTEMBER 17, 1683]

"I then most always saw, with great wonder, that in the said
matter there were many very little living animalcules, very
prettily a-moving. The biggest sort had the shape of Fig. A: these
had a very strong and swift motion, and shot through the water
(or spittle) like a pike does through the water. These were most
always few in number.

"The second sort had the shape of Fig. B. These oft-times spun
round like a top, and every now and then took a course like that
shown between C and D: and these were far more in number.

"To the third sort I could assign no figure: for at times they
seemed to be oblong, while anon they looked perfectly round. These
were so small that I could see them no bigger than Fig. E.: yet
therewithal they went ahead so nimbly, and hovered so together,
that you might imagine them to be a big swarm of gnats or flies,
flying in and out among one another."

LET US NOW move ahead almost 200 years in time, into the 19th century. The compound microscope has been brought to such a state of perfection that biologists can now see and differentiate not only the animalcules discovered by Leeuwenhoek, but even details inside their bodies. Little by little an unexpected picture comes to light. First, biologists find the microscopic world incredibly rich and varied; it consists of an immense number of different types of creatures which, despite their minute size, have all sorts of extraordinary shapes and move in all sorts of extraordinary ways. In comparison with the intense and agitated life that can be seen with the microscope in a hanging drop of pond water, the usual world of things visible to the unaided eye looks very quiet indeed!

What is even more extraordinary is the fact that protozoa, algae, microscopic fungi, bacteria, and other lowly creatures which used to be regarded as very primitive, almost as undifferentiated chunks of protoplasm, in reality turn out to be very complex after all. In most respects, they are in fact as complicated as the constituent cells of our own body. This was not a sudden discovery. Rather the descriptions published during the past 100 years show that the structural complexity of microorganisms dawned very progressively on the minds of biologists. In truth, the picture is not yet complete because more and more unexpected facts are being discovered all the time. Let us examine a few examples which will convey, I hope, some idea of the incredible variety and strange beauty of the microscopic world.

As mentioned earlier, Leeuwenhoek himself had recognized different shapes among bacteria and had illustrated them by drawings in the letters I have quoted. To convince ourselves of the acuity of his vision, we need only compare his pictures drawn from what he saw through his one-lens microscope with modern photomicrographs taken at very high magnification. There is no difficulty in relating the various bacterial types to those that Leeuwenhoek had seen.

It is even more enlightening to watch living bacteria in the actual process of growth and division. The extraordinary speed at which

[FROM LEEUWENHOEK'S LETTER OF SEPTEMBER 1692]

"I saw, too, sundry animalcules that had very near the same length, and also some a bit longer. These moved their bodies in great bends, in comparison of the first animalcules, and made with their bendings so swift a motion, in swimming first forwards and then backwards, and particularly with rolling round on their long axis, that I couldn't but behold them again with great wonder and delight . . . .

"Furthermore, I saw animalcules that were of very near the same thickness, but of singular length. These had so little motion that I had most times to confess they might not be living creatures at all; yet when I could keep my eye on them, without getting tired, I could make out that they bent their body very slow, just bending it into a very faint curve, so that they didn't move forward, or very little. These animalcules, as they looked to me, are shown in Fig. C.

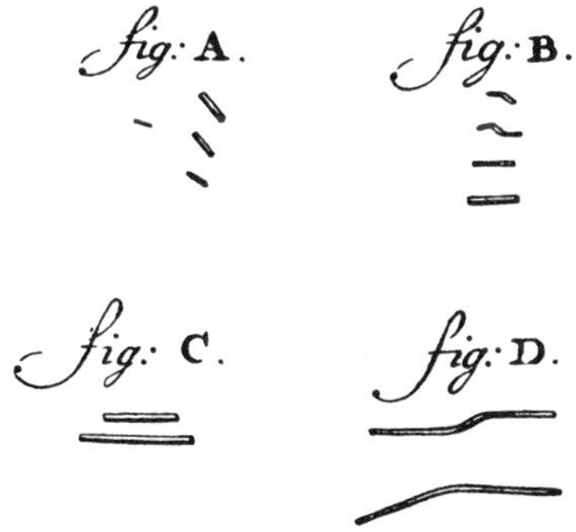
fig: A.
fig: B.
fig: C.
fig: D.

"Now I also saw yet other animalcules, that were of very nigh the same thickness, but which in length even surpassed those last described. But you seldom saw two of this sort alongside, or floating off in the wet stuff, that were of one and the same length. These animalcules too were in great numbers, whereof some were straight, while others had a kink in them, as shown in Fig. D."

some bacteria, in fact most of them, enlarge and divide is the first thing that catches attention. It is not at all unusual to see a bacterial cell double its size, and divide into two daughter cells, within half an hour! The process of bacterial multiplication reveals furthermore that the mode of division differs from one type of bacteria to another. For example, some cells are spherical and divide in such a manner that they give rise to characteristic groups resembling bunches of grapes. This is true of the staphylococci (the most common cause of boils and carbuncles), and, in fact, *"staphylo"* is the Greek word for grapes. In contrast, other spherical cells form long chains, as in the case of streptococci. (*Strepto* means "like a twisting chain or neck-lace" in Greek.) Many bacteria are elongated and are called for this reason bacilli (the plural from the Greek word *"bakyla"* meaning sticks or rods). When bacilli continue to adhere to each other end to end, after division, they commonly produce long chains which may fold in all sorts of extraordinary festoons. For another illustration of the very characteristic physical traits of various types of bacteria we can look at spirochetes, organisms which are corkscrew shaped with different intensities of winding. The organisms which cause syphilis, relapsing fever and yaws, for example, belong to this general group.

The differences in form between one bacterial group and another are so striking that experienced bacteriologists can often make an approximate identification from a rapid glance at the appearance of a group of bacterial cells under the microscope. This can be done with living bacteria suspended in a hanging drop and observed preferably with dark-field illumination. Morphological identification is also possible with dead bacteria stained with dyes on a glass slide. In this case the staining characteristics supplement the information provided by size.

Another visual character of great usefulness in differentiating one bacterial species from another is motility. Some bacteria can move about freely and rapidly—as Leeuwenhoek reported in such picturesque words — whereas others appear to be motionless. Micro-cinematography reveals that there exist several mechanisms of loco-

12

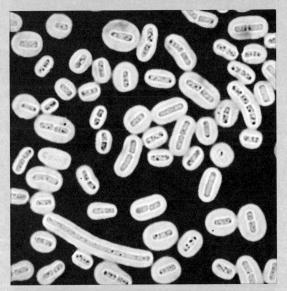

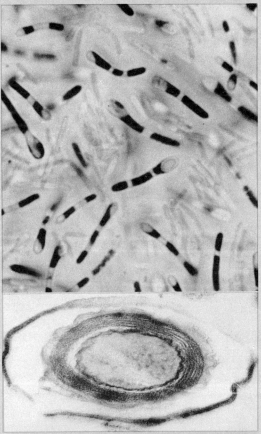

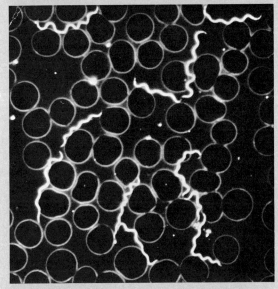

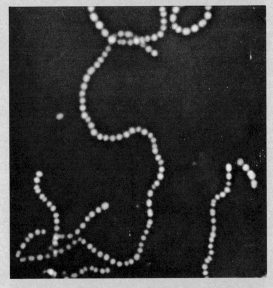

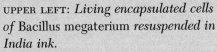

UPPER LEFT: *Living encapsulated cells of* Bacillus megaterium *resuspended in India ink.*

LOWER LEFT: Borrelia duttoni, *the agent of African relapsing fever, among red blood cells.*

UPPER RIGHT: Clostridium pectinovorum, *dispersed in Lugol's iodine solution, showing sporing forms. The lower part of the illustration is an electron micrograph of a section through a spore of* Bacillus megaterium, *showing a concentric array of fine fibrils in the cortex.*

LOWER RIGHT: *Chains of* Streptococcus pyogenes.

13

motion among bacteria. A few bacterial types exhibit flexuous movements of the whole cell. Others move by means of threadlike appendages — called flagella — which may be single or numerous according to the bacterial species under consideration, and which may occur only at one end of the cell, or at both ends, or all over its surface.

THE EXISTENCE OF all these contrasting shapes, modes of division, and types of motility is incompatible of course with the view that bacteria are simple, undifferentiated bits of protoplasm. And

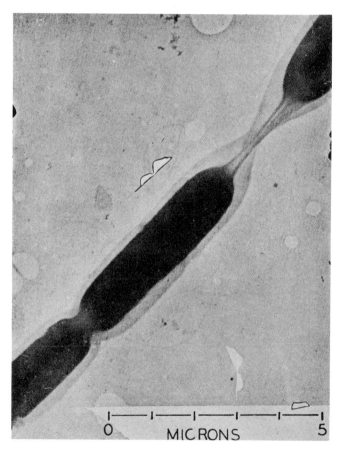

Electron micrograph of Bacillus cereus, *showing the cellular wall and the protoplasmic bridge between two cells.*

14

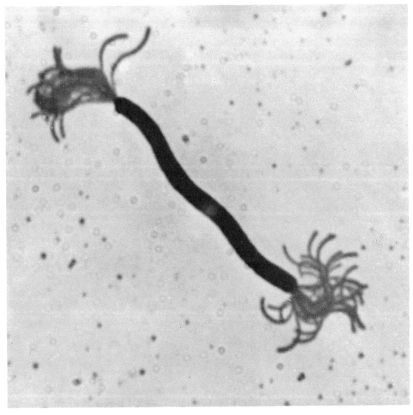

Stained preparation of Spirillum serpens, *showing bushy tufts of flagella.*

indeed, the more one studies bacterial cells, the more numerous and varied are the structures they reveal. For example, mucilaginous capsules surround many kinds of bacteria; a semi-rigid cell wall protects their protoplasm; then there are the flagella which we have already mentioned, and which are present only in motile forms. All these structures have long been well identified; indeed their constituents have been analyzed chemically. But in addition there exist also internal granules which are less well known and which, in fact, have attracted the attention of microbiologists only during recent years. Some of these granules — called mitochondria — are rich in enzymes and are the seat of important biochemical activities of the cell. Other granules appear to be the equivalent of the nucleus in ani-

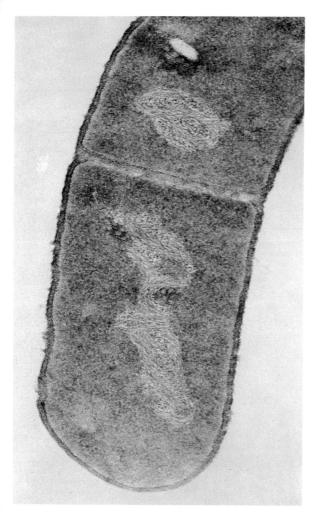

LEFT: *Two cells of* Bacillus subtilis *with their respective nuclear structure. Notice that the lower cell shows the nucleus in the process of undergoing division.*

BELOW: *Electron micrograph of section through tetrad coccus showing nuclei.*

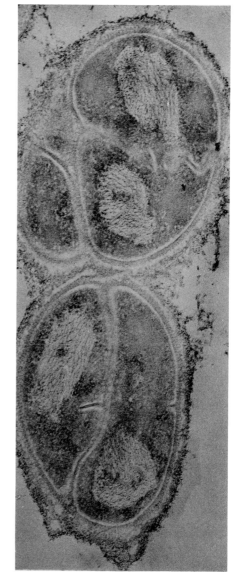

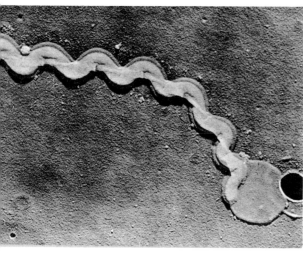

ABOVE: Leptospira icterohemorrhagiae. *Electron micrograph of a preparation shadowed with chromium. It shows a protoplasmic spiral and axial filament, a covering sheath, and a terminal bulb (the black structure at the extremity is an artifact).*

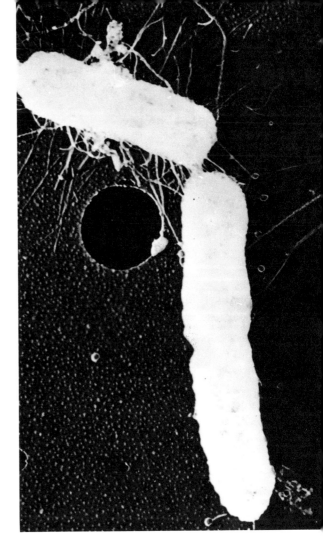

In this electron micrograph two Escherichia coli *cells of opposite types are seen to undergo conjugation. The genetic material is transferred from one cell to the other through the cytoplasmic bridge.*

mals and plants, which means that they are the bearers of hereditary characteristics.

While we are on the subject of heredity, let us consider some very recent findings which further illustrate the complexity of bacterial life. A few years ago, it was observed that in certain bacterial cultures one could see now and then two individual cells unite, with a resultant mixing of their intracellular contents. This phenomenon seems to be rather rare, but it can be convincingly demonstrated by careful microphotography. What gives special significance to this bacterial conjugation is the fact, revealed by genetic analysis, that certain bacteria can exchange hereditary

17

traits by sexual union just as do higher organisms. In brief, it seems justified to believe that bacterial conjugation corresponds to a mechanism of sexual reproduction not unlike sexuality in higher animals and plants.

Let me emphasize again that bacterial conjugation is probably a rare event and therefore is extremely difficult to observe. In contrast, its equivalent can be seen readily in certain molds and fortunately it has been recorded in excellent motion pictures. Consider, for example, the life of a certain mold of the kind commonly seen on objects become moldy in humid atmosphere. In the most common phase of its life, the mold spreads and invades new territory through the production of a threadlike structure which is called the mycelium. Then there appear along the mycelium specialized bodies which bear reproductive cells known as spores.

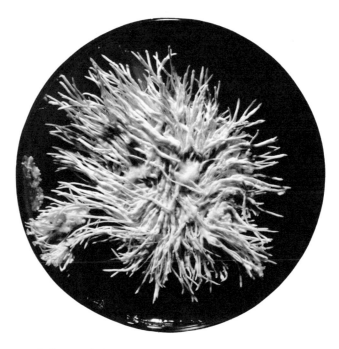

Colony of the mold Isaria cretacea, *a parasite of insects. This strain was isolated from soil.*

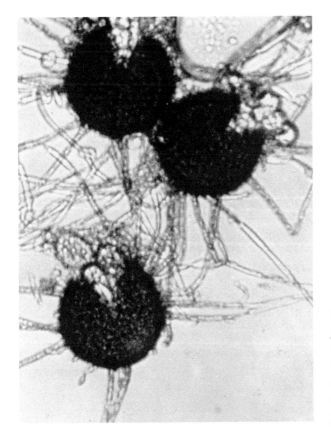

Spores being discharged from specialized reproductive bodies produced by fungus mycelium. Under favorable conditions, these spores germinate and produce a new growth of the fungus.

These are released into the external environment, ready to germinate and give rise to a new growth of mycelium whenever conditions are favorable for their germination.

The production of ordinary spores does not involve any sexual process; in fact, it is little more than a simple fragmentation of the mycelium. But now and then something much more complicated takes place. A strand of the mycelium which we may call the positive or male organ, surrounds a particular cell which constitutes its negative or female counterpart. The two fuse together, thus giving rise to an entirely different kind of structure which possesses hereditary characteristics of both cells from which it was made. The genetic aspects of this primitive sexual union in molds have been studied in great detail, and there is no doubt that they correspond

19

in all essentials to what happens in higher plants and animals.

As already mentioned, sexual reproduction in microorganisms is far less frequent than reproduction by simple division. Among bacteria in particular, growth takes place chiefly by fragmentation of each cell into identical parts. Nevertheless, the existence of sexuality among lower organisms makes it clear that we must entirely dismiss from our minds any thought that microscopic size corresponds to a primitive manifestation of life. Bacteria are not made up of undifferentiated protoplasm. It is only their small size which has concealed for so long the extraordinary complexity of their organization.

MANY DISCOVERIES remain to be made with ordinary microscopy using ordinary light, especially by taking advantage of the proper staining techniques which provide information as to the chemical constitution of the various cellular components. But whatever the technical improvements, objects much smaller than one-thousandth of a millimeter (about 4/100,000th of an inch) cannot be seen with the ordinary microscope, because of the fundamental limitation imposed by the wave length of light. This limitation in magnification has been overcome during recent decades by the use of the electron microscope, an instrument which uses not a beam of light, but an electron beam of a wave length much shorter than that of light and which produces pictures on a fluorescent screen. As the electron microscope can give enormous magnifications — in theory up to ten thousand times more than the light microscope — it is now possible to recognize details of cellular structures that could not be detected with the light microscope. For example, the bacterial cell walls and the flagella can now be seen to possess a delicate submicroscopic structure. Even more exciting, however, is the fact that by the use of electron microscopy it has become possible to study the shape and nature of filterable viruses — those mysterious submicroscopic agents which have puzzled biologists ever since Pasteur discovered that one of them was the cause of rabies.

20

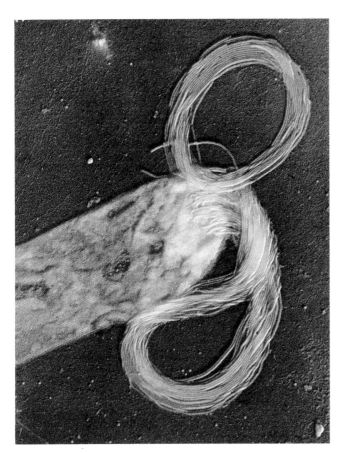

LEFT: *Electron micrograph of Spirillum sp. (Houwink) showing in detail the attachment of flagella to the cell and their complex structure.*

BELOW: *Electron micrograph of the cell wall from a crushed preparation of Spirillum sp. In some parts, the inner membrane has come off, revealing the inner face of the wall and providing evidence of a two-sided cell membrane.*

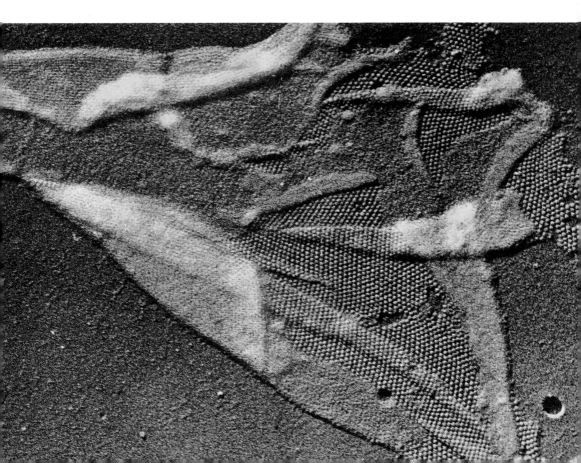

For three-quarters of a century, scientists have known that many diseases of man, animals, plants and even of microorganisms are caused by transmissible agents which cannot be seen under the light microscope, and which moreover are so small that they can pass through filters fine enough to hold back the most minute bacteria. These mysterious invisible agents were given the generic name of viruses long before one knew anything about them beyond the fact that they can multiply in certain living things as if they themselves were living. In the 1930's, two great discoveries were made which provided concrete information concerning the nature of viruses. On the one hand, it was found that some of them can be crystallized almost as readily as if they were ordinary chemical substances. Chemically, the active virus particles were found to behave like giant molecules. At about the same time, the electron microscope became available and permitted pictures to be obtained of these crystals as well as of particles present in fluids and other materials known to have virus activity. And behold! viruses could now be seen as concrete objects instead of being merely imagined as abstract concepts.

The first unexpected fact revealed by electron microscopy was that the various viruses differ among themselves in shape and in size, as much as do the various types of bacteria. Just as the bacteriologist can recognize at a glance through the light microscope to what morphological group a bacterium belongs, so can the virologist differentiate between several types of viruses on the basis of their size and shape as revealed by electron micrographs. For example, the vaccinia virus is rather large, almost within the range of resolution of light microscopy. In contrast, the polioviruses are much smaller and yield very characteristic crystals. As to the tobacco mosaic virus, it can be crystallized in the form of thin needles having different lengths. The viruses that attack bacteria, which are called bacteriophages, are more complex, at least in shape. Many of them are sperm-like with a thin tail and a large round or cylindrical head.

The remarkable diversity of size and shape exhibited by viruses

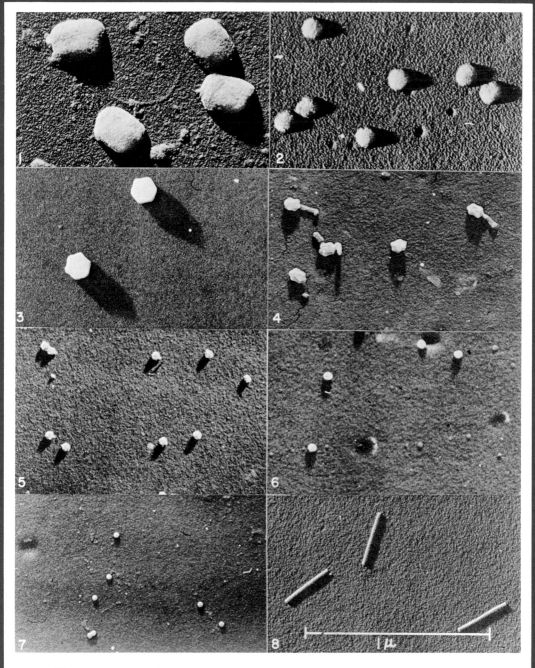

Electron micrographs of 8 viruses shown at the same magnification (× 50,000)

1 *Vaccinia virus*
2 *PRB influenza virus*
3 *Cytoplasmic virus of* Tipula poludosa
   (R.C. Williams and K.M. Smith)
4 *T4 bacteriophage*
5 *T3 bacteriophage*
6 *Shope papilloma virus*
7 *Poliomyelitis virus*
8 *Tobacco mosaic virus*

Micrographs 3 to 7 show frozen-dried preparations. Micrographs by R. C. Williams; virus preparations: (1) by R. C. Williams; (2), (6) and (8) by C. A. Knight; (4) and (5) by D. Fraser; (7) by C. E. Schwerdt and F. L. Schaffer, all of the Virus Laboratory, University of California, Berkeley.

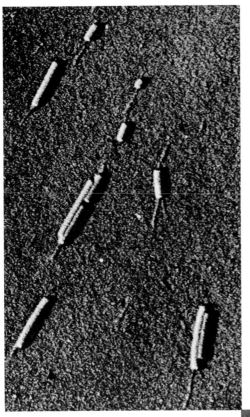

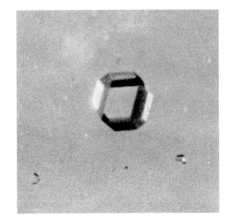

Large octahedral crystal of virulent poliomyelitis virus. This was the first human virus to be obtained in crystalline form.

ABOVE: *Individual particles of tobacco mosaic virus showing extrusion of the ribonucleic acid core from the protein coating.*

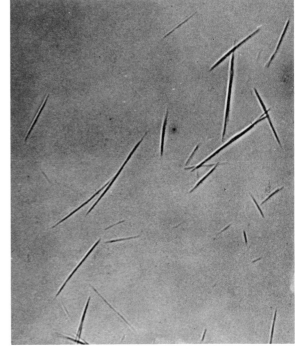

RIGHT: *Nucleoprotein crystals of tobacco mosaic virus. These crystals have the great historical interest of having provided the first evidence of the crystalline structure of viruses.*

Electron micrograph of frozen crystals of poliovirus at approximate magnification of 100,000. Similar ordered arrays of particles have been observed with many other viruses.

goes hand in hand with a chemical complexity much greater than had been expected. As mentioned above, a number of viruses have now been crystallized, and it is this fact which has facilitated the study of their chemical composition. As far as can be judged at the present time, each active virus particle consists of at least two very different types of structural components and often of many more. One structure made up of nucleic acid, carries the genetic hereditary characteristics of the virus. Another, protein in nature, is thought to protect this genetic apparatus and to facilitate its transfer from one infected cell to another. For example, electron micrographs have revealed that the virus of tobacco mosaic consists of

an inner constituent of nucleic acid lodged as it were within an outer coat, cylindrical in shape and made up of protein. The central structure, the core, might be compared to the nucleus of ordinary cells in higher organisms, which also contains large amounts of nucleic acid and also carries the genetic endowment. In fact, there is evidence that the nucleic acid core of the virus is its most essential constituent. However, proteins and nucleic acids are not the only structural components of active viruses. Certain viral particles have recently been shown to contain lipids as part of their essential structures. High-magnification electron micrographs reveal furthermore that some of them possess a distinct membrane.

In the light of this very new knowledge, it is clear that we must

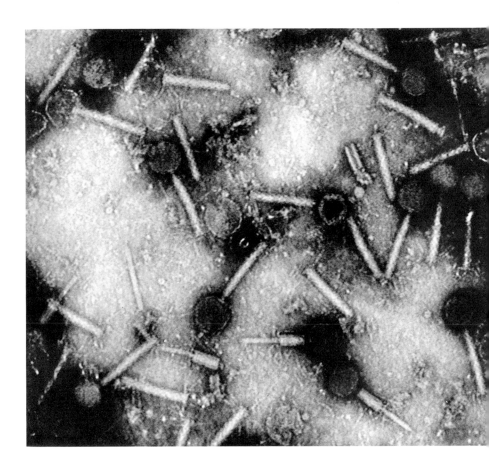

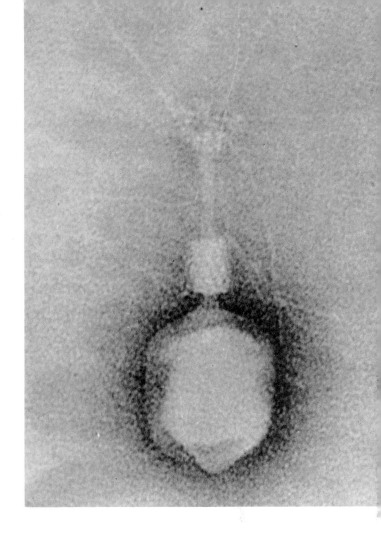

Electron micrograph of a bacteriophage particle showing: the "head" which serves as the protein envelope for the nucleic acid, the tail fiber which determines the host range of the strain, the tail "core" through which the nucleic acid is injected into the bacterial cell.

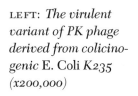

LEFT: *The virulent variant of PK phage derived from colicinogenic* E. Coli K235 *(x200,000)*

change our views concerning the nature of viruses; we can no longer regard them simply as giant molecules. It is still true of course that one can handle viruses in the laboratory — at least some of them — as if they were only giant lifeless molecules. The beautiful crystalline arrangement exemplified on page 25 is not an exception. Equally striking crystalline patterns have been encountered time and time again during the study of other viruses capable of attacking men, animals, plants, or bacteria.

It is true also that many viruses can be purified by orthodox chemical techniques as if they were defined substances, like hormones or enzymes. Furthermore, it has become apparent during recent years that size cannot be used as a criterion to differentiate

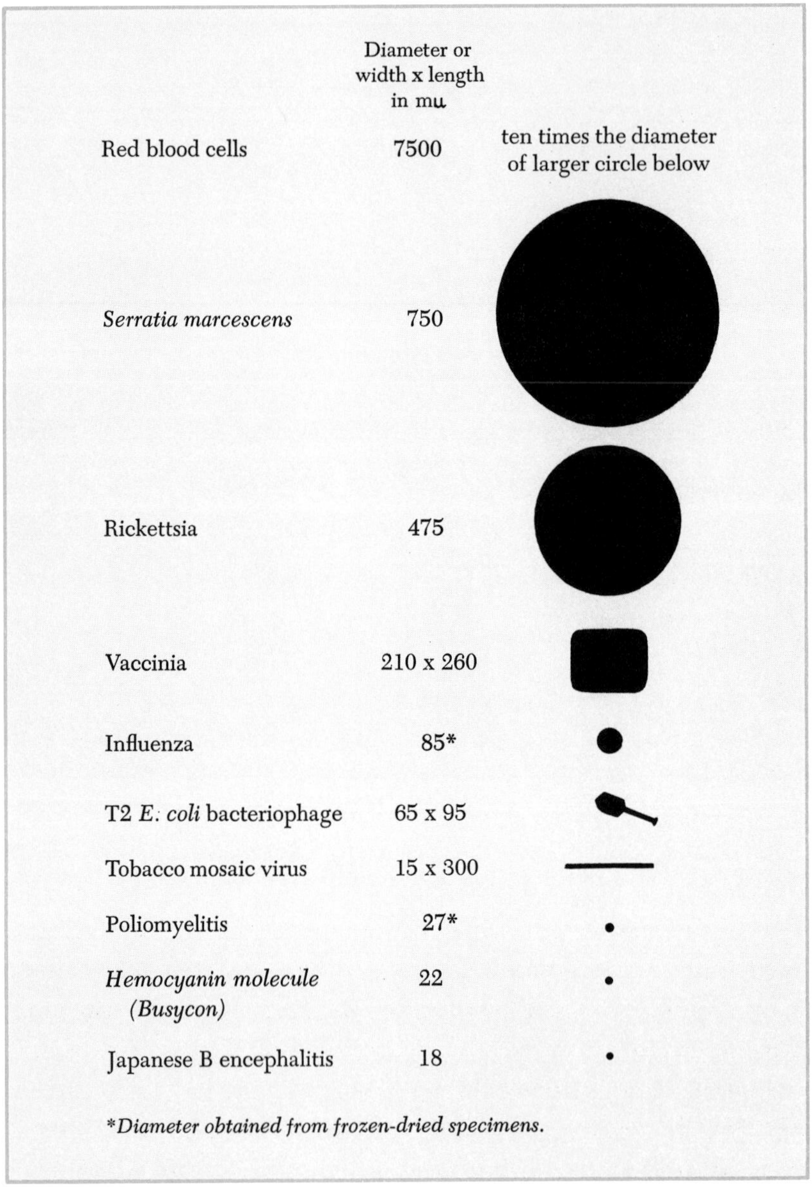

	Diameter or width x length in mμ	
Red blood cells	7500	ten times the diameter of larger circle below
Serratia marcescens	750	
Rickettsia	475	
Vaccinia	210 x 260	
Influenza	85*	
T2 *E. coli* bacteriophage	65 x 95	
Tobacco mosaic virus	15 x 300	
Poliomyelitis	27*	
Hemocyanin molecule (Busycon)	22	
Japanese B encephalitis	18	

Diameter obtained from frozen-dried specimens.

Comparative size of protein molecules, viruses, rickettsia, bacteria and red blood cells. The chart shows that the smallest viruses are no larger than the hemocyanin protein molecule, and that there exists an unbroken continuity of dimensions from the molecular world to the most complex living forms.

viruses from inanimate molecules. For example, the viruses which cause Japanese B encephalitis or tobacco necrosis measure approximately 16 mμ in diameter, a size not very different from that of the horse hemoglobin molecule which is 15 mμ in length and 3 mμ in width. Indeed, one type of molecule (hemocyanin) has been shown to measure 22 mμ in diameter and thus to be larger than the smallest known viruses, and of the same size as the yellow fever virus. As seen in the chart on the facing page, there exists an unbroken continuity of dimensions from the inanimate to the living world.

In contrast to these similarities certain other facts do seem to set viruses apart from even the largest molecules. One needs only look at the electron micrographs of the bacterial viruses (bacteriophages) shown on pages 26 and 27 to know that here are structures which have the morphological attributes of living organisms. They are surrounded by membranes, are divided into inner and outer parts, and possess peculiar appendages; one might even suppose that they can wiggle. Furthermore, experiments reveal that all known kinds of viruses can undergo mutations and thereby adapt themselves to new hosts, new temperature ranges — in other words to new living conditions. The chemist can indeed manipulate some viruses as he does giant lifeless molecules, but the biologist can elicit from them reactions which call to mind many traits characteristic of living things.

Shortly after the preceding lines were written, there appeared a short article demonstrating that the so-called Eaton virus — an agent responsible for some cases of atypical pneumonia in man — could be made to multiply on a lifeless artificial culture medium. Thus, what was called last year the Eaton virus now turns out to be a living organism after all. It belongs to a group of microbes known among microbiologists as PPLO (pleuropneumonia-like organisms) which have very exacting growth requirements and among which are found the smallest things so far shown to be capable of independent life. Who can be unimaginative enough to assume that future research will not reveal the existence of still smaller living things?

It was only a few decades ago that we had to dispel the illusion that bacteria were made up of undifferentiated protoplasm. Today's research is revealing that all viruses also are complicated structures, and that some of them, at least, may be really living things rather than lifeless crystals. The rapid changes in point of view that have occurred recently regarding the structure of bacteria and viruses teach an important lesson in scientific humility. It is always dangerous to be dogmatic, overconfident in the finality of one's knowledge. The concepts of even the most learned and perceptive scientists are limited by the means of observation available to them, and the most advanced theory is nothing more than the best approximation to truth at a given time.

The wisest thing that can be said of science and the most encouraging, in my judgment, is that "it continually opens new fields to our vision" and that it "progresses stepwise to levels of more and more subtle understanding." These last two statements are not mine. They were made 75 years ago by Louis Pasteur, the very great scientist who established the role of microbial life in the general economy of nature, and whose work we shall discuss in the next chapter.

CHAPTER TWO

Microbes as
Chemical Machines

O NE OF THE FIRST materials in which Leeuwenhoek saw
bacteria under his microscope was an infusion of pepper. The entertaining reason he gave for having looked at this material was that he
wanted to "discover the cause of the hotness or power whereby
pepper affects the tongue"! He was apparently expecting to see
sharp barbs which would explain the irritating property. Needless
to say, Leeuwenhoek did not find why pepper is hot to the tongue,
but having discovered the microbial world instead, he continued
to observe it just for curiosity's sake. In this he displayed the attitude
of the true scientist who takes advantage of any accidental observation to probe into the mysteries of nature.

For 150 years after Leeuwenhoek, many microscopists all over
Europe spent countless hours and an immense amount of ingenuity
describing and classifying various kinds of microorganisms, yet
without realizing that some of these played an important role in
the practical affairs of man. I mention this fact to illustrate that much
of science has its origin in plain disinterested curiosity, in the sense

*Microscope used
by Pasteur*

of wonder that makes adults as well as children observe strange mosses, migrating birds, or heavenly bodies.

Many scientists of course differ greatly from Leeuwenhoek in their approach to the problems posed by nature. Some want above all to find the theoretical explanation of puzzling phenomena; they are primarily concerned with the laws that govern the Universe. Others in contrast are most interested in solving problems that have to do with the welfare of mankind or with the creation of wealth and of power; they apply their efforts to the practical applications of science. Needless to say, these different types of scientific attitudes often co-exist in the same person. This was true of Louis Pasteur, whose work is of immense importance in several areas of microbiology.

One of the many interesting aspects of Pasteur's scientific life is that he had received his advanced training not in biology, but in physics and chemistry. In fact, his first great achievements had been in physical chemistry. He won his first laurels at the age of 23 when, as a graduate student, he made fundamental contributions to the chemical theory of molecular structure. As this subject appears far removed from microbiology, we must examine the manner in which Pasteur's initial discoveries in crystal structure eventually proved of importance for the study of microbes.

When Pasteur started research work for his doctor's degree, it was already known that the solutions of tartaric acid produced naturally during the fermentation of wine rotate the plane of polarized light, whereas those prepared by chemical synthesis are optically inactive. In order to investigate this puzzling fact, the

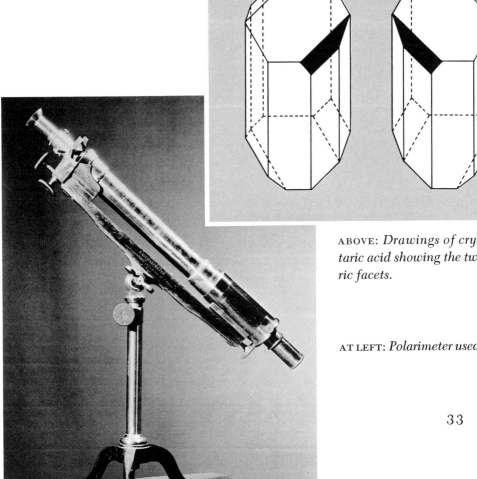

ABOVE: *Drawings of crystals of tartaric acid showing the two asymmetric facets.*

AT LEFT: *Polarimeter used by Pasteur.*

33

young Pasteur crystallized different salts of tartaric acid and compared their chemical and physical properties. Placing the various tartrates that he had prepared under the microscope, he noticed that the preparations which were optically inactive yielded crystals which were rather odd in shape. In brief, there seemed to be two kinds of crystals, one kind having small facets oriented to the right with relation to the axis of symmetry, another kind having the same kind of facets but oriented to the left. With infinite care Pasteur proceeded then to separate the two kinds of crystals — with small forceps manipulated by hand under the microscope, mind you! When he made solutions of each kind of crystals, he found that one solution deviated polarized light to the right, and the other to the left. Furthermore, when he prepared solutions containing equal amounts of the two crystals, the mixtures proved to be optically inactive.

The relation of optical activity to crystalline structure probably seems rather simple and obvious to persons who have studied modern organic chemistry. However, the magnitude of Pasteur's achievement becomes impressive when one realizes that he was totally unprepared for his findings because there was no knowledge of this field 100 years ago. Moreover Pasteur had at his disposal only a very primitive microscope and polarimeter. No surprise, then, that upon recognizing the relation of optical activity to crystalline shape, he literally ran out of his laboratory shouting in excitement. It is apparent that Pasteur could not have detected the difference between the two types of tartaric crystals if he had not been a very acute observer, and more importantly if his mind had not been bent on finding some fact that would explain the difference in optical activity between the two kinds of tartaric acid.

Very rapidly Pasteur went on with his work on crystallography, and he soon became immensely impressed by the fact that many materials produced by living things are optically active, whereas similar organic substances synthesized in the laboratory by chemical means are always optically inactive. It is now known that the reason for this difference in optical activity resides in the fact that labora-

34

Professor of Chemistry in Strasbourg in 1852

As a student at the École Normale

Dean of Sciences in Lille in 1857

tory synthesis always yields mixtures made up of equal weights of molecules having opposite optical activity. We shall soon recognize the decisive influence of this awareness on the subsequent course of Pasteur's work.

Before proceeding with this aspect of the problem, however, it will be worth looking at a photograph of Pasteur taken during his graduate school years. It reveals clearly, it seems to me, the determination of his character, and even more the thoughtfulness and concentration that he applied to everything he did. It was by dedicating himself to his problems, by becoming completely absorbed in them, that he succeeded in linking together in his mind facts that appeared at first sight unrelated. Thus, he was led to all sorts of ingenious original hypotheses. And then, he never hesitated to convert his ideas into experiments, however trying and unfavorable were the circumstances under which he had to work.

Pasteur's imagination was well served by unusual powers of

Pastel portraits of his parents done by Pasteur at age 13 and 15.

observation as was illustrated in the preceding paragraphs by his ability to detect minute differences in shape between the two crystalline forms of tartaric acid. In this regard it is of interest to note that while still a schoolboy he had made some twenty remarkable portraits of members of his family and of friends. These portraits, now on exhibit in the two Pasteur museums in France, reveal not only great care and technical skill, but also an ability, astonishing in such a young person, to perceive significant aspects in the personality of the sitter. The portraits of his father and mother which are reproduced here were colored drawings in pastel that he made when he was about fourteen years old.

At the age of 35 Pasteur was appointed professor of chemistry and dean of sciences in a newly organized branch of the University at Lille in the north of France. He was then a stern, serious-minded scholar, passionately interested in scientific research, but also very mindful of his social duties. His appointment at the University of Lille carried the stipulation that he was to direct the attention of his students to the scientific aspects of the industrial and agricultural activities of that part of France. Some scientists would probably have resented this directive as a limitation on their intellectual independence, but such was not Pasteur's bent. In fact, as we shall see, he lived up to the demands made upon him, and he managed also to use the study of the practical problems that he encountered in the north of France as a springboard for the prosecution of his own theoretical interests. Throughout his life, he was wont to emphasize that "There are not two kinds of science — practical and applied. There is only Science and the applications of Science, and one is dependent on the other, as the fruit is to the tree."

THE PRODUCTION of alcohol from the juice of the sugar beet was one of the important industries of the north of France. Shortly after Pasteur's arrival in Lille, an industrialist of that city sought his advice regarding the fact that the alcohol produced in his plant by the fermentation of beet juice was contaminated with other undesirable substances. The industrialist had good reason to consult a

37

professor of chemistry on this problem, because it was then believed that fermentation was a purely chemical process, in which yeast acted merely as a chemical reagent converting the sugar into alcohol.

Surprisingly enough it was Pasteur's early work in crystallography that helped him recognize the nature of the phenomena responsible for defective alcoholic fermentations. One of the observations that provided him with the necessary clue was the finding that the industrial alcohol produced by the fermentation of beet juice was contaminated with large amounts of optically active substances. This fact called back to his mind the observations that he had made with tartaric acid ten years before. He postulated that the various substances produced during fermentation did not arise from simple, ordinary chemical processes, but rather originated from the activities of some kind of living agent. Even though Pasteur was a chemist by training, this thought made him look at the problem of fermentation from a biological point of view. As a consequence he began a careful microscopic examination of fermenting material in the hope of finding more direct proof of the presence therein of living organisms.

Very rapidly Pasteur came to the view that yeast was not merely a chemical catalyst, but in reality a microscopic living plant. He postulated furthermore that the production of alcohol was the result of the biological activity of yeast, and that the defects in fermentation were caused by other kinds of microorganisms which acted on the sugar of beet juice and produced substances different from alcohol. With extraordinary intuition, he suggested in fact that a bad alcoholic fermentation was one that had a sort of disease caused by certain microorganisms. And giving full rein to his imagination he went as far as expressing his belief that diseases of animals and men also would eventually be shown to be caused by microorganisms. These were marvelous guesses, and because they all came out to be right, they can be regarded as the beginning of the germ theory of fermentation and of disease. But it took many, many years to prove their validity and to work out in detail the manifold activities of microorganisms in nature.

38

In 1857, Pasteur returned to Paris where he had been appointed director of scientific studies at his alma mater, the École Normale Supérieure. Immediately he took up his research work again in an attempt to prove that microbes are around us all the time — in the air and on every object that we touch. However, he found it difficult to prove this theory to his opponents — and there were many of them. For no one at the time was ready to believe that ordinary air or clear water contained invisible living things, and it was even more difficult to imagine that these could be responsible for the chemical changes occurring in sugar solutions or could bring about the spoilage of foodstuffs. Of the many ingenious techniques that Pasteur devised to prove his point, I shall mention only one, namely the use of peculiarly shaped glass vessels, which he called "swan neck" flasks.

He introduced a fermentable fluid, for example beef bouillon,

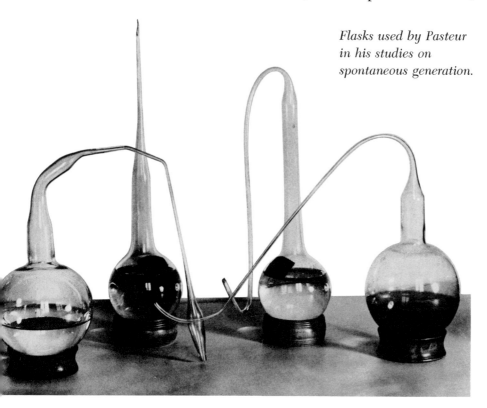

Flasks used by Pasteur in his studies on spontaneous generation.

The small attic room at the École Normale which Pasteur used as a laboratory for his studies on spontaneous generation.

into a long neck flask of which he then drew the neck into the form of a sinuous S tube (hence the name "swan neck flask"). The liquid was boiled, the vapor thus forcing out the air through the orifice of the neck. On cooling, the air slowly returned to the flask, but in so doing it came into contact with the moisture that had condensed in the curves of the neck after the administration of heat had been interrupted. Under these conditions, the air was washed free of dust and of other particles and the fluid in the flask remained clear, sterile. But if the neck of the flask was broken immediately after heating, the air rushed in and came into contact with the fluid without first being washed. As a result, microscopic life soon developed in the flask — thus demonstrating the presence of microorganisms in the air.

Pasteur also carried out many experiments to determine the relative abundance of microorganisms in the air. By taking air samples at various places and bringing them into contact with nutrient bouillon, he found that microbial life was very abundant in the atmosphere of a dusty, crowded yard in Paris, less so in a deep cellar

40

where the air had been allowed to remain still, and even less on glaciers in the mountains away from plant growth and human dwellings.

Most of Pasteur's early work after his return to Paris was carried out in a very primitive laboratory improvised in the attic of the École Normale — from which he emerged now and then to collect air samples in his flasks. These fundamental experiments established that microbes exist everywhere all around us, and that they do not generate spontaneously *de novo* in natural fluids — a knowledge that constitutes the very basis of modern medicine and of biological technology. It is very inspiring indeed to think of this attic laboratory and thus to create a mental picture of the very humble environment in which began so much of modern microbiology.

DESPITE THEIR intrinsic elegance and simplicity, the experiments on spontaneous generation were but an aside to Pasteur's main thesis. What he really was bent on demonstrating was that microbes play an essential part in the economy of nature and in the life of man. We shall discuss in subsequent chapters the role of microbes in the causation of disease and in industrial processes. For the moment we must limit ourselves to the discussion of their activities as chemical machines and describe the manner in which they carry out so many profound and surprising transformations of organic and inorganic matter. As it happens, some of the most illuminating examples of chemical reactions brought about by microorganisms are provided by Pasteur's own discoveries; and to understand the problem, we cannot do better, therefore, than to retrace some of the ground he covered one hundred years ago.

In 1857, Pasteur published a short paper entitled "Sur la fermentation appelée lactique." This document is of extraordinary historical importance because it can be regarded as the manifesto of the germ theory of fermentation. In his 1857 report Pasteur showed that the souring of milk is caused by microbes which convert milk sugar into lactic acid, the acidity thus produced in turn clotting the casein of milk. This change in milk can be caused by streptococci, as usually occurs under natural conditions, or by lactobacilli, as in the case of commercially produced yogurt or acidophilus milk. But in all cases the process is fundamentally the same and can be chemically expressed as follows:

$$C_6H_{12}O_6 \rightarrow CH_3CH_2COOH$$
$$\text{(sugar)} \qquad \text{(lactic acid)}$$

In its gross result and in appearance at least, this is one of the simplest chemical changes that can be imagined, representing as it does the breakdown of one molecule of sugar into two molecules of lactic acid.

Let us now turn to another transformation of sugar studied by Pasteur during the same period, namely alcoholic fermentation as exemplified by the conversion of grape juice into wine. In this case, as is well known, the microorganism responsible for the change is

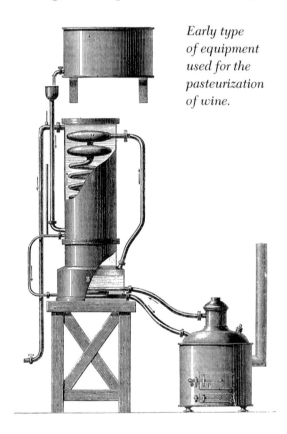

*Early type
of equipment
used for the
pasteurization
of wine.*

42

yeast, which converts the sugar of grape juice into alcohol according to the following equation:

$$C_6H_{12}O_6 \rightarrow CH_3CH_2OH + CO_2 + H_2O$$

(sugar)   (alcohol)

When left exposed to the air, wine will turn into vinegar, and this is precisely the next problem to which Pasteur addressed himself. He showed that in this case the change is caused by still another type of microorganism, a bacterium now called *Acetobacter*, which oxidizes alcohol into acetic acid according to the following formula:

$$CH_3CH_2OH + O_2 \rightarrow CH_3COOH + H_2O$$

(alcohol)   (acetic acid)

As we have just seen, the conversion of sugar into lactic acid or alcohol occurs independently of the presence of oxygen, whereas the conversion of alcohol into acetic acid results from an oxidation which involves the participation of atmospheric oxygen. In contrast, Pasteur observed that when a sugar solution was placed in an atmosphere from which the oxygen had been completely removed a very different kind of substance was likely to appear, namely butyric acid. Under these conditions, the bacteria which proliferate (*Clostridium butyricum*) live best without oxygen and in fact may die in the presence of this gas. "Anaerobic" bacteria (to use an expression invented by Pasteur himself) convert sugar into butyric acid according to the following formula, which corresponds to "anaerobic" fermentation, that is one not involving the use of oxygen.

$$C_6H_{12}O_6 \rightarrow CH_3CH_2CH_2COOH$$

(sugar)   (butyric acid)

I have listed these four different types of chemical processes, not only to demonstrate the range of Pasteur's contributions to microbial chemistry, but even more to illustrate the chemical versatility of microorganisms. The important lesson to be derived from these simple examples is that, given a certain substance, it can be transformed into many different derivative substances depending upon the types of microbes to which it is exposed, and upon the particular conditions under which microbial action takes place.

43

Pasteur's fundamental discovery that each type of microbe is more or less specialized in a few chemical reactions has found its counterpart in the fact that, for every kind of organic substance, there exists in nature at least one and usually several kinds of microorganisms capable of attacking this substance provided the conditions are right. The biological explanation for the Biblical statement that "to dust thou shalt return" is thus to be found in the fact that organic matter does not accumulate in nature under normal circumstances. The many types of microorganisms that are present almost everywhere in nature break down all complex organic substances stepwise into simpler and simpler chemical compounds. They constitute so many indispensable links in the endless chain which binds life to matter and matter to life. Without them life would soon come to an end.

To illustrate by a simple operation the universality of this law of nature, one need only add any kind of organic material to soil or sewage water. More or less rapidly the substance decomposes and eventually disappears completely. Paper constitutes a convenient substance for this test. When placed in contact with soil and sewage, the surface of the paper invariably becomes covered with all kinds of bacteria, actinomycetes, or fungi — many of them brilliantly colored. These microorganisms grow on the paper because they have the power of attacking cellulose — the chemical of which paper is made. In fact, these microorganisms are also capable of attacking cellulose in the test tube if some soil or sewage is added to dilute solutions of inorganic salt and ammonium sulfate in which paper has been immersed. Within a few days or weeks, the paper disintegrates, attacked chiefly by fungi if the culture medium is slightly acidic, by bacteria and actinomycetes if it is neutral or slightly alkaline. Further evidence of the immense role that microorganisms play in the economy of nature is found in the fact that, according to recent calculations, the total mass of microbial life on earth is approximately *twenty times greater* than the total mass of animal life! Truly, in Pasteur's own words: "The role of the infinitely small in nature is infinitely great."

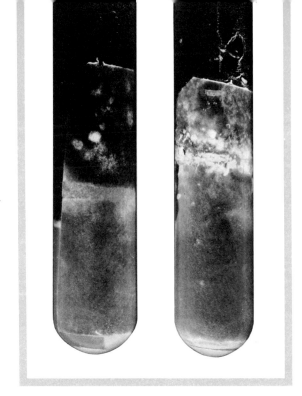

Two test tubes containing filter paper (cellulose) in a simple mineral solution. The tubes were inoculated with small amounts of soil. LEFT: *This tube contained an acidic solution in which the cellulose is attacked by soil fungi.* RIGHT: *This tube contained a neutral solution in which the cellulose is attacked by soil bacteria.*

E VER SINCE PASTEUR, increasing numbers of microbiologists and biochemists have continued to investigate the chemical activities of microorganisms. And as a result of their studies, it has become clear that many of the chemical processes that occur in the microbial world are very similar to those that occur in plants, animals, and men. For example, the chemical phenomena that provide energy for muscle contraction or nerve action are similar to the reactions by which yeast and other microorganisms transform sugar into lactic acid and alcohol. Likewise, the iron-containing pigments which are essential for respiration in man and animals also are essential for the performance of the microbial processes which utilize oxygen — such as the conversion of alcohol into acetic acid in vinegar making. It follows as we shall see later that the toxic substances which paralyze respiration in man and animals are also poisonous for the bacteria which utilize oxygen.

Another chemical similarity between microbes and higher organisms is found in their enzymes, the complex substances which activate biochemical processes in all living tissues. In man and animals,

45

enzymes are needed to digest the various foodstuffs that reach the stomach and the intestines, as well as to carry out all other biochemical activities in the different organs. And likewise, microorganisms possess enzymes which enable them to make proper use of the various kinds of food. A simple and striking illustration of this fact is provided by the ease and rapidity with which gelatin and starch are liquefied, not only by living bacteria and molds, but also by soluble extracts prepared from cultures of those microorganisms which contain their enzymes. In fact, it can be said that practically all enzymes found in animal and plant tissues have their counterpart in the microbial world.

During recent decades scientists working on microbial nutrition have found that vitamins provide still further evidence of similarity among the different forms of life — from the largest to the smallest. It must be said in truth that many microorganisms can grow in culture media deficient in the vitamins required for the survival and growth of animals and men. But the reason is that these microorganisms can themselves synthesize the vitamins from simpler materials, and thus produce enough to satisfy their own needs. In other words, whether microorganisms do or do not require preformed vitamins for growth, they utilize these substances for their biochemical activities in much the same way as do plants, animals, and men.

From all these facts, there emerges the very important law that all living things share in common a large number of essential biochemical properties. In fact, it can be said that the recognition that there exists a fundamental unity of biochemical processes in all living forms, constitutes a scientific generalization of great philosophical significance. This generalization can be regarded as one of the most important contributions of microbiology to theoretical science and to philosophy.

There is another aspect of the microbial world that is worthy of special emphasis here, namely its amazing chemical versatility. In the examples considered so far, we have barely scratched the surface of the chemical activities that can be recognized in the microbial world. Whatever the type of chemical reaction one has in mind, the

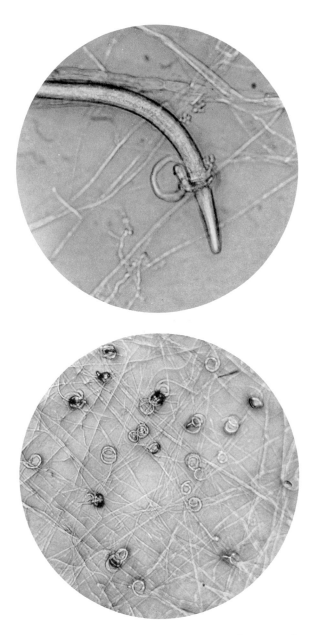

TOP: *Soil nematode* Neoaplectana glaseri *trapped in mycelium coils of the predaceous fungus* Arthrobotrys conoides. *Following strangulation of the nematode the fungus digests its body.*

BOTTOM: *The fungus* Arthrobotrys conoides *normally does not produce the coils when grown in broth in the absence of the nematode. However, these coils can be produced experimentally by adding to the fungus culture a soluble extract of the nematode.*

chance is fair that somewhere in nature there exists some species of microorganisms capable of carrying it out. For example, there exist bacteria which can oxidize suspensions of elementary sulfur into sulfuric acid. They derive energy from this reaction and require for their growth only some mineral salts and carbon dioxide in addition to sulfur. Remarkably enough, some bacteria perform this extraordinary chemical feat at very high temperature in certain hot springs of Mexico. They provide a striking contrast to other types of bacteria recently brought back from the Arctic and the Antarctic, which grow readily at icebox temperature.

In the folklore and literature of the past, there were many legends associated with the will-o'-the-wisp — the mysterious eerie light seen hovering at night over marshy lands. Few people believe in the existence of the will-o'-the-wisp nowadays, and yet the legends have some basis in fact. In the depths of marshy lands where oxygen is lacking, there exist anaerobic bacteria which produce methane (CH_4) from the cellulose and sugars in decaying plants, and also phosphine (PH_3) from organic materials rich in phosphorus. As methane and phosphine are volatile and can ignite in the air, it is not impossible that the legends of the will-o'-the-wisp have their origin in the light produced by the ignition of these bacterial products. It would be difficult to reproduce this phenomenon in a lecture room, but it is relatively simple to demonstrate indoors another kind of bacterial light produced under conditions opposite to those associated with the will-o'-the-wisp.

Certain luminous bacteria of the genus *Photobacterium* grow readily in sea water and at room temperature. They produce light when oxygen is available to them and the luminescence of their cultures is so strong that it can be readily observed in the dark. Light production can be demonstrated by placing in a flask large numbers of luminous bacteria resuspended in a neutral phosphate solution containing 0.5 per cent glycerine with 3 per cent sodium chloride (a high concentration of sodium chloride is needed because the bacteria originate from the sea and are therefore best adapted to high saline concentration). After the room has been darkened, and the

Flasks containing agar medium with an abundant growth of the lumines-cent bacterium Photobacterium fischeri. *The photograph, taken in the dark, shows the silhouette of a microscope against the luminescent glow produced by the bacteria (exposure 4 minutes on Agfa Isopan Record).*

eyes have become dark accommodated, an eerie glow can be caused to appear in the flask by agitating its contents in order to aerate the bacterial suspension.

As I mentioned a while ago, the production of light by *Photobacterium* requires oxygen. For this reason, the light becomes dimmer as soon as agitation of the flask is interrupted, the amount of oxygen available to the bacteria then decreasing and soon falling below the critical point. In contrast, light becomes more intense again as soon as shaking is resumed.

The dependence of light production on oxygen utilization can be made even more striking by another experiment. Let us introduce into the flask a small amount of sodium azide, one of those poisons I mentioned earlier which paralyze respiratory processes by interfering with oxygen utilization. The flask becomes dark shortly after sodium azide has been added, and this time, no amount of shaking can restore light production, the reason being that even though oxygen is present in the flask, it can no longer be utilized by the poisoned bacteria. Note in passing that this phenomenon provides another illustration of the biochemical similarity in respiratory processes between bacteria and higher organisms.

Many other kinds of tests could be arranged to illustrate the chemical versatility of microorganisms. But one more class of examples will have to suffice — namely their ability to produce bright pigments from the simple nutrients provided to them in ordinary culture media. An easy way to demonstrate pigment production is to grow the proper kind of bacteria on the surface of nutrient agar. Within one or a few days, depending upon the specific culture used, there appear on the agar surface brilliantly colored bacterial colonies which are red, pink, orange, purple or iridescent. The particular color obtained is characteristic for each strain of microorganism and for the conditions of growth. The chemically minded bacteriologist can extract the various bacterial pigments, purify and crystallize them, even determine their molecular composition. For bacteriologists in a more playful mood, it is entertaining to arrange the pigments in color patterns or even to make with them pictures of houses, animals, or young girls in gay dresses. Amusingly enough some such pictures were made a number of years ago by the illustrious bacteriologist Sir Alexander Fleming, the discoverer of penicillin. I mention this fact, not only for its historical interest, but also to illustrate once more that the chemical activities of microorganisms can serve many different purposes. They can be used to materialize in color the fanciful dreams of scientists — old as well as young — just as they can serve admirably to illustrate profound scientific and philosophic truths, among them the biochemical unity of life.

50

CHAPTER THREE

The Germ Theory
of Disease

L‍ET US TURN BACK in time one hundred years, and try to imagine how we would have reacted then if some science fiction writer had asserted that many of the most important fatal diseases of man, animals, and plants are caused by microscopic and sub-microscopic creatures. Unquestionably, we would have been skeptical, and indeed scornful as everyone else was at that time. There is at first sight something incongruous in the thought that a delicate microbe, toothless and spineless, so small as to be invisible, can kill a tree, an ox, or a man. Yet this thought has become commonplace to-day, and we can safely assume that almost everyone now believes that viruses, bacteria, and many other types of microorganisms are capable of causing disease. It must be recognized, however, that this belief is a matter of hearsay and of faith, rather than first hand knowledge based on the kind of personal and direct experience which makes one know that fire burns and that glass cuts. For this reason, it will be useful to examine first the factual evidence which justifies this faith. To a very large extent, this evidence is derived from the pioneering studies of Louis Pasteur (1822–1895), Joseph Lister (1827–1912), and Robert Koch (1843–1910) — the three giants who ushered in the period which has been called "The Golden Era of Medical Bacteriology."

As mentioned in the preceding chapter it was in 1857 that Pasteur first formulated the germ theory of fermentation and of disease, and this is why I suggested a moment ago that in imagination we turn the clock of time back 100 years. With wonderful perspicacity, Pasteur had perceived that his findings with regard to the role of microbes in fermentation were probably relevant to the problem of infectious disease. Although his 1857 paper dealt primarily with the conversion of sugar into lactic acid he was bold enough to state that just as microorganisms can multiply in organic solutions, thereby causing chemical changes, likewise they might multiply in the body of living things and thereby cause disease. It was with this theory in mind that he later used the expression "diseases of wine and of beer," to designate the alterations in the quality of these beverages brought about by various microorganisms. Then from 1867 to 1870 he studied two important diseases of silkworms and he established that in these cases protozoa and bacteria were the responsible agents. The practical importance of the new theory was made obvious by the fact that it led Pasteur to work out an effective program of control of the silkworm diseases.

Pasteur's discoveries on the chemical activities of microbes came to the attention of the English surgeon, Joseph Lister, who saw in them a possible explanation of many of the accidents that were then so commonly encountered in surgical practice. Lister surmised that the microbes shown by Pasteur to be ubiquitous in the air could fall on open wounds and thus be responsible for the phenomena of "putrefaction" and of "sepsis" that were the cause of immense numbers of fatalities in surgical wards at that time. Acting on this theory, Lister made it a practice to spray a solution of phenol around his patients in an attempt to sterilize the air during operations, and thus he greatly decreased the rate of fatal surgical infections. Lister's work constituted a very great practical achievement, the first con-

*Sir Joseph Lister,
(1827–1912), at 69
years of age. He was
born in England.*

scious and successful application of the germ theory to the preven-
tion of diseases of mankind. Surprisingly enough, however, his
results did not at first impress the medical world, and physicians
failed to recognize their relevance to other disease conditions.

In order to understand the failure of the public and of the medical profession to appreciate fully the significance of Lister's work, it
must be realized that the idea that microbes can cause damage
to the body seemed then contrary to common sense. Likewise, the
thought that the earth is round had appeared incompatible with the
experience of the senses a few centuries earlier. Common sense is
what is commonly believed, but this does not necessarily make it
good sense. One of the greatest merits of experimental science is that
it constitutes a technique to examine the validity of *a priori* assump-

53

tions. Thus experimental science helps mankind to come nearer to reality by dispelling the fog of errors and superstition through which all of us look at the objects and events of the external world.

The view that microbes can cause disease in man was outside the range of direct human perception one hundred years ago. However, it became an accepted concept once the limited knowledge of disease that had been gained by observations with the unaided senses was broadened by the laboratory experiments that Pasteur and Koch started around 1875. Almost simultaneously and unknown to each other, Pasteur and Koch both became at that time interested in anthrax, a disease that was — and still is — common and often fatal in farm animals, and also of some importance in man.

A FTER GRADUATING from medical school in 1866, Robert Koch practiced medicine for a few years. In 1872 he established his office in the small town of Wollstein in Posen, northern Germany. He was then an unknown young man of 23 and found himself isolated, far removed from any medical school or scientific institute, and with meager financial resources. But this did not deter him from undertaking research work in the then new science of bacteriology, the rudiments of which he had learned at the University of Göttingen. He built a laboratory in his own home and there, without help, developed wonderful new techniques to observe bacterial growth in vitro, and also to produce experimental infections in animals.

The old house where Koch began his work has now become a museum. It retains the atmosphere in which so much of modern medical bacteriology was originated from experiments conducted with primitive equipment and simple techniques. At first, Koch used kitchen plates as his laboratory glassware, and potato slices as nutrient surfaces on which to grow bacteria. With homemade microphotographic equipment, using illumination from a beam of sunlight passing through a hole in the wooden shutters, he learned to take pictures of bacteria, and thus obtained photomicrographs which have hardly been excelled to the present time. Experimental animals

This is the room in his own house which Robert Koch converted into a laboratory. To the left is the homemade photographic equipment with which he took the first photomicrographs of anthrax bacilli and tubercle bacilli. On the tables are the very simple objects — many of them obtained from his kitchen — that he used as equipment for his celebrated studies on the role of microorganisms in disease causation.

had to be housed in crude cages on book shelves among small jars containing the glass slides and dyes needed for staining bacteria and infected tissues. By modern standards, the working room was primitive and crowded with inadequate equipment, but it was permeated with the most important ingredient of science, an atmosphere of intense concentration, of determination, and of learning.

Seen from the vantage point of today's knowledge, Koch's scientific achievement appears as simple as the techniques he used in his homemade laboratory. He first demonstrated that a certain type of microorganism — now known as *Bacillus anthracis* — is always present in the tissues of animals suffering from anthrax disease; he cultivated the anthrax bacilli in drops of serum and on glass slides covered with blood clot; this permitted him to observe microscopically in great detail, and also to photograph, the growth of the bacilli outside the body. Then he injected into animals some of the bacilli that he had cultivated in serum and he thus managed to reproduce at will a disease similar to anthrax. Furthermore, he demonstrated that the experimental production of the disease was always associated with the multiplication of the anthrax bacilli in the blood and in the various organs of the infected animals. The most impressive aspect of his achievement is that the several procedures that he worked out to establish the bacterial causation of anthrax are still considered today, with modifications to fit each individual case, essential to demonstrate the causative role of a particular microorganism in a particular disease.

The technical perfection and elegance of Koch's studies on anthrax immediately placed him at the forefront of Germany's medical scientists, and he was given a position of importance in Berlin as well as a large laboratory. There he applied his precise bacteriological techniques to several of the most destructive diseases of man, and within a very few years he acquired everlasting fame by two dramatic achievements: the discovery of the tubercle bacillus in 1882 and of the cholera vibrio in 1883.

Many portraits are available to illustrate Koch's spectacular career. The early photographs reveal that his self-confident and determined personality was already well developed during his days as a student and as a young adult. At the age of 40 he had taken the appearance of a stern Geheimrat ruling with authority over his Institute in Berlin. A photograph of him in a Japanese costume symbolizes the immense fame that was his when he visited Japan, where he was treated as a demi-god, and where a shrine was dedicated to him.

From the point of view of medical history, Koch's most spectacular achievement was to discover tubercle bacilli and to prove that

56

Robert Koch during the 1907 expedition in Bugala to study African sleeping sickness.

Monument in honor of Robert Koch in Japan.

Robert Koch with his wife, in Japanese costumes.

they can cause tuberculosis in man and in animals. Tuberculosis was the most important disease of the 19th century in Europe and it is still common today. In fact, tuberculosis is so prevalent in Asia, Africa and South America that it constitutes the most important disease of mankind as a whole; it is the modern plague of the under-privileged parts of the world. This makes it worthwhile to outline here some of the modern lines of work presently being pursued in many institutes all over the world to analyze the precise mechanisms of tuberculous infection.

There are many ways to study tuberculosis in experimental animals. The most common is to introduce tubercle bacilli into the body of mice, rats, guinea pigs, rabbits, etc., and to observe the development of the lesions in the various organs of the infected animals. The bacilli can be introduced with a syringe into the blood stream or into the muscles; or they can be spread by an atomizer into the air of a closed chamber in which the animals are placed. By means of this latter technique of so-called airborne infection, experimental animals can be made to inhale tubercle bacilli into their lungs by breathing, and thus caused to become infected in much the same manner as do human beings. These techniques have provided in the past, and are still providing today, much important information concerning the development of tuberculosis, but they are not sufficient to answer some of the questions concerning the precise manner in which tubercle bacilli become established in the body.

One of the most difficult problems is to determine what happens to the bacilli when they first enter the body. It is known that during the very first phase of infection there are no lesions to be seen, no obvious signs of disease, just a few bacilli coming into contact with a few body cells. Yet this very beginning of the infectious process is of enormous importance because it influences, and indeed often determines, the subsequent course of events. I have selected for discussion this particular phase of tuberculosis because the problems that it poses apply to all other infectious diseases as well, and the new techniques that have been developed to study it are of very general application in medical research.

58

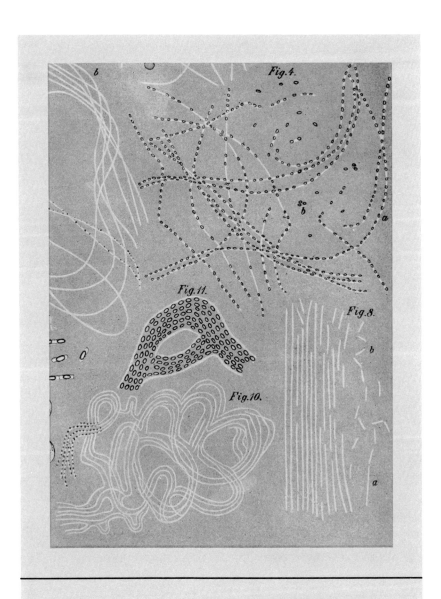

Part of a plate prepared by Robert Koch to illustrate his celebrated publication on anthrax (1877). The plate shows both vegetative and sporing forms of Bacillus anthracis, *at various stages of development. Notice groups of bacilli end to end in long festoons.*

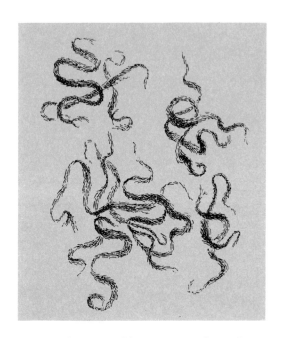

Plate illustrating Robert Koch's celebrated publication on tuberculosis. Note that the individual bacilli are arranged in a serpentine pattern. It is now recognized that this arrangement is characteristic of the virulent forms of tubercle bacilli.

Three quarters of a century ago, Elias Metchnikoff (1845–1916), discovered that many cells in the blood and in the various organs have the power to engulf the small particles with which they come into contact — a process that he called phagocytosis. Thus, when tubercle bacilli are introduced into the body either artificially by injection, or in natural infection by breathing, they are taken up by the phagocytes in the blood, in the lungs, and in other tissues. The same process of engulfment also takes place in vitro when the proper types of tissue cells and the bacilli are placed together in an adequate medium. For example, phagocytosis can be demonstrated by adding a few tubercle bacilli to a drop of blood, or to a small fragment of spleen placed on a glass slide. Under these conditions, the interplay between the various types of living tissue cells and the living bacilli can be followed by microscopic observation, indeed can be recorded step by step by time-lapse cinematography.

60

Refinements of technique now permit use of a single bacillus, introduced by micromanipulation and followed for many days to observe what happens to this bacillus and its descendants as they grow in the presence of the various types of body cells. In other words, it is now possible to obtain a continuous picture of the very earliest phase of the infectious process, at least in these so-called "tissue cultures" in vitro.

What has been found under these conditions is that the tubercle bacilli are engulfed almost immediately by white corpuscles—the phagocytes. In some cases the bacilli fail to multiply and die in the phagocytes, and thus the infection of the tissue culture spontaneously comes to an end. In other cases, the bacilli get the upper hand, multiply within the phagocytes, destroy them, and as a result the infection spreads throughout the culture. If we generalize from what happens in tissue culture to what happens in the body, and this generalization is probably justified, it follows that the outcome of the infection is decided in part during the early struggle that takes place beween the invading bacilli and the phagocytic cells that engulf them.

This struggle between tissue cells and bacteria can be observed not only in the case of tuberculosis, but also in every other type of bacterial disease. For example, one can study phagocytosis from photomicrographs and motion picture films illustrating the engulfment of streptococci by blood phagocytes. In fact, there is no doubt that phagocytosis represents one of the most important mechanisms by which the body defends itself against all sorts of infection. If the phagocytes succeed in keeping the bacteria under control then the infected individual remains healthy, but serious disease develops whenever the bacteria gain the upper hand.

It must be emphasized, however, that engulfment of microbes by phagocytes is not the only mechanism that the body has at its disposal to defend itself against infection, for there exist in the tissues and body fluids many kinds of antimicrobial substances which also play an important protective role. One of these substances, lysozyme, was discovered by Sir Alexander Fleming several years before he discovered penicillin; it is capable of rapidly killing several types of bacteria. Still more important is the fact that there appear in the blood during infection other substances, known as antibodies, which are specifically active against the particular kind of microbe responsible for the infection. In fact, infection elicits the production of many different kinds of antibodies which react selectively with the various components of bacterial cells, viruses and other micro-organisms. During typhoid fever, for example, or as a result of injection of typhoid vaccine, there are produced antibodies which combine with the flagella of the typhoid bacillus, and other antibodies which combine with components of its cell wall. The study of these antibodies, of their constitution, properties, and biological role, is extremely complex and constitutes a special body of science called immunology.

MICROORGANISMS CAN cause disease not only in man and animals, but also in plants. Interestingly enough, this fact was recognized long before Pasteur and Koch had begun their work. Although it was their studies on anthrax which convinced the world of the germ theory of disease, the fact is that the first demonstration of the theory occurred around 1845 at the time of the great potato famine in Ireland.

On several occasions during the 1840's, the potato crop in Ireland was ruined by a disease called the potato blight. As a result of the ensuing famine, the Irish population fell within a decade from 8 million to 4 million. Approximately one million Irish people died at that time of outright starvation, and some 3 million had to leave their impoverished country, many of them emigrating to America. Studies carried out during the 1840's showed that the blight was caused by a fungus, *Phytophthora infestans*, which multiplied abundantly in all parts of the potato plants when foggy, humid days prevailed during the early period of the growing season.

The potato blight provides a tragic illustration of the human sufferings that can result from a fungus disease of plants. But many other plant infections are just as destructive and economically im-

62

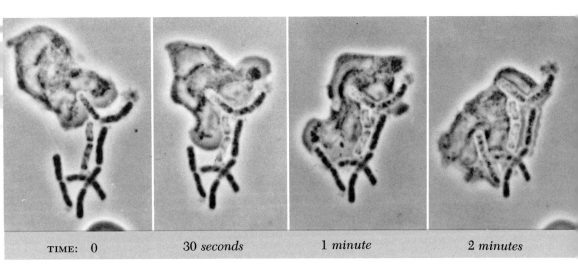

| TIME: 0 | 30 *seconds* | 1 *minute* | 2 *minutes* |

Consecutive steps in the phagocytosis of Bacillus megaterium *cells by a white blood cell (polymorphonuclear leucocyte) obtained from human blood (phase microscopy, magnification 2000).*

portant, among them the wheat rust which constantly threatens the wheat crop in the Middle West, and the chestnut blight which has almost completely eliminated this beautiful tree from the American woodland. Among plant diseases, I shall mention one more example because it will be considered again in the following chapter. It concerns ergot, an infection caused by a fungus that attacks rye and turns its grain into a black mass made up of the fungal growth. In only rare cases does ergot completely destroy the rye harvest, but its importance as a cause of disease is very great nevertheless. This is due to the fact that the fungus produces a substance which is so toxic that persons who eat bread made from the contaminated flour are poisoned and may die, even though only a small amount of diseased rye grain is mixed with the healthy grain. Ergotism, as the disease in man is called, takes many forms, all the way from gangrene of the legs to terrible spasms and other extraordinary nervous manifestations. It was so common in early days that many illustrations of it have come down to us, usually showing the patients being helped by Saint Anthony, whose name was given to the disease.

63

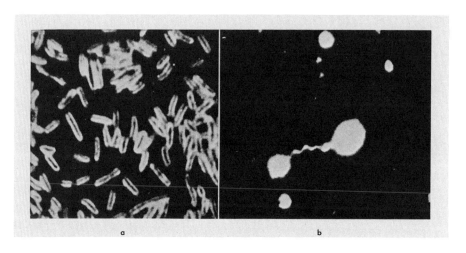

Darkground photomicrographs illustrating agglutination of typhoid bacilli by specific antibody directed against the flagella. a) Normal non-agglutinated bacilli; b) early phase of agglutination. Note granules on flagella resulting from deposition of antibody.

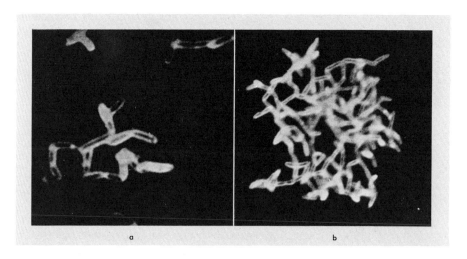

Darkground photomicrographs illustrating agglutination of typhoid bacilli by specific antibody directed against the bacterial cell wall. a) Early stage of agglutination showing bacilli joined together by their ends; b) completed agglutination.

So FAR, I have discussed examples of diseases caused by bacteria and by fungi. But many parasitic protozoa also can attack man and animals. One of them causes malaria, a disease responsible for an immense amount of physical hardships and economic misery throughout the world. Other protozoa cause African sleeping sickness in human beings; a similar protozoan disease in cattle is so destructive that it is largely responsible for the lack of meat and milk in tropical Africa.

Among agents of disease the filterable viruses occupy the limelight at the present time in the Western World — and for very good reasons. I need only mention the common cold, influenza, the various forms of encephalitis, paralytic poliomyelitis, infectious hepatitis, yellow fever, etc., to give an idea of the wide range of afflictions for which viruses are responsible. Naturally, I cannot discuss these sub-

The 1845 potato famine in Ireland. This contemporary woodcut depicts the starvation and misery that resulted from the complete destruction of the potato crop by the fungus Phytophtora infestans.

jects in detail here because there would be too much to say and because a discussion of them, even though superficial, would call for a highly specialized kind of medical knowledge. Suffice it to state that more and more scientists — microbiologists, chemists, as well as physicians — are becoming deeply interested in viral infections at the present time because these infections present some of the most important and interesting problems of modern biology and medicine.

I shall single out for consideration one particular kind of virus infection which is of great scientific interest because of the many unexpected and exciting discoveries to which it has given rise during recent years. These infections are caused by special viruses, called bacteriophages, which attack bacteria and cause in them a fatal dis-

Ergotism, also called St. Anthony's Fire. This woodcut by Johannes Wechtlin (1490–1530) illustrates the gangrene caused by consumption of ergot, a poisonous substance produced by the growth of the fungus Claviceps purpurea *on rye. The bones of the hermit Saint Anthony were assumed in the Middle Ages to miraculously cure the disease.*

ease — just as other kinds of viruses cause fatal diseases in the cells of plants, animals, and men.

The phenomenon of bacteriophagy was recognized for the first time forty years ago when it was noticed that certain filterable materials could cause the disintegration — bacteriolysis, it is called — of bacterial cultures. It was then found that as a result of destruction of the bacteria by bacteriophage, there was produced in the culture fluid more filterable material capable of causing further lysis of new bacterial cultures. This spectacular phenomenon long remained very mysterious because bacteriophages are so small that they cannot be seen under the light microscope. But now, electron microscopy permits us to visualize the multiple reactions through which bacteriophages disintegrate bacterial cells.

In a first step, the bacteriophage becomes attached to the bacterial cell, apparently by anchoring its thin part — the so-called tail — on the bacterial membrane. Then the nucleic acid constituent of the bacteriophage head penetrates into the bacterial body and reproduces in it the full bacteriophage. Finally, this complete bacteriophage multiplies in the cell to such an extent that approximately 100 new identical particles are produced. Then the bacterium bursts and the bacteriophage particles are liberated. All this complex process usually runs its course in no more than 30 minutes and by this time most of the bacteria are dead and disintegrated! It is this disintegration that accounts for the clearing — bacteriolysis — of cultures infected with bacteriophage.

ON THE BASIS of all the facts outlined in this chapter it has become possible to formulate a concept of the germ theory of disease far more comprehensive than the picture first perceived by Pasteur and Koch. What their pioneering studies had shown was that microbes of all sorts can attack and kill large and complex living things, whether they be plants, animals, or men. Then later it was discovered by other microbiologists that microbes can in fact multiply within the individual cells of which these complex living things are made. And now we find that bacteria themselves, even the very kind that are capable of causing disease in man, animals or plants, can likewise be attacked and killed by small viruses.

Scientists, and microbiologists in particular, can well be proud of having discovered such extraordinary phenomena and of having thrown so much light on the struggles that go on between the microbial world and all living things. But lest modern scientists become too conceited, it is good for them to remember that in some way all this had been foretold long ago. Many ancient physicians had guessed on the basis of shrewd clinical observations that certain diseases spread through the agency of minute particles which they called "miasmas" and which they knew were commonly present in the air and in water. And it was more than two centuries ago that Jonathan Swift wrote the famous lines:

> "So, naturalists observe, a flea
> Has smaller fleas that on him prey;
> And these have smaller still to bite 'em;
> And so proceed *ad infinitum.*"

Two conjugating cells of Escherichia coli. *One of them (right) is being attacked by bacteriophage. Notice that the other (left) belongs to a strain of* E. coli *which is resistant to this bacteriophage.*

69

CHAPTER FOUR

The Domestication
of Microbial Life

T H E F A C T S concerning the germ theory of disease that we discussed in the preceding chapter may have given the impression that all microorganisms are potential threats to the well-being of man, and that in consequence the best course is to eliminate them altogether from our environment. In reality, nothing could be further from the truth, for most microbial species are completely innocuous under ordinary conditions; furthermore, as we have seen, some of them play an essential role in the economy of nature. Equally important is the fact that man makes use of microbial life for all sorts of practical ends and that he depends on it for his very survival, just as much as he does on plant and animal life.

Very early and empirically, man learned to take advantage of some of the chemical transformations of matter brought about by microbes. Some of these practical applications of microbial life to human affairs are very peculiar indeed. For example, ochre, which occurs as scum or precipitate in wayside ditches, has its origin in the action of microorganisms on iron compounds, and served during prehistoric times to decorate household objects and even the human body. These precipitates of microbial origin, being very rich in iron, are still useful today because they provide excellent raw material for iron smelting wherever they are available in large quantities, as in bog iron ore.

Of much greater importance is the fact that man has developed techniques to cultivate microbes for special purposes instead of relying on their spontaneous, uncontrolled activities in nature. This domestication of microbial life is certainly very ancient. In Biblical times, and probably even among the most primitive people, yeast was used to ferment grape or barley juice into wine or beer, and to raise the dough into leavened bread. Since these remote days, the arts of alcoholic fermentation and of bread making have remained essentially unchanged, but the large scale industrial operations derived from them would not have been possible without modern scientific knowledge.

Consider, for example, the production of yeast. From time immemorial bakers used "leaven" left from the previous day's work to cause the new batch of dough to rise. We now understand that what the baker thus achieved unwittingly was to carry active yeast from one batch of dough to the next. Likewise, wine makers and beer brewmasters trusted to the fact that the proper kind of yeast would develop — spontaneously as it were — in grape juice and in malted barley exposed to the proper conditions in the proper place. In the past, and not a very distant past at that, bakers, vintners and brewmasters thought that the development of yeast was a natural occurrence, and they had no conception of why things went wrong now and then in their traditional processes when the bread, wine or beer was spoiled. We now understand that these accidents are caused by the multiplication of microorganisms other than yeast which produce undesirable substances when they gain the upper hand.

Yeast is still an essential component in the modern technology of bread making, wine fermentation, or brewing, but its supply and its use are no longer left to chance. In the large scale industrial plants of today, different kinds of yeast are carefully selected for each par-

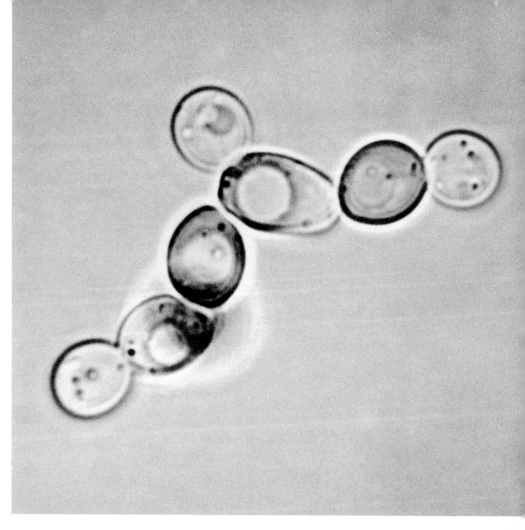

Photomicrographs of yeast cells. The series below shows four consecutive pictures of the same yeast cell, taken over a total period of fifteen minutes, and illustrating the progressive development of a bud. In the last picture, the wall of the parent cell has been rebuilt, and the bud is ready to break away and begin an independent existence.

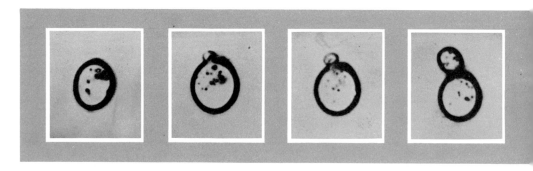

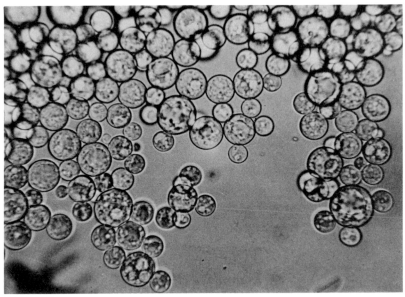

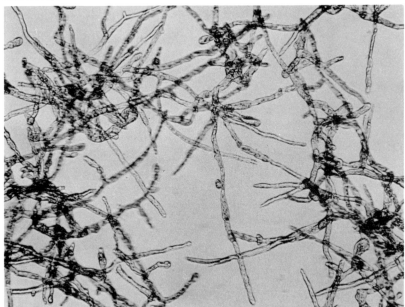

Two photomicrographs of the same fungus Mucor Rouxii *grown for 48 hours at 28° C, but under different conditions. The filamentous growth is obtained when the medium is flushed continuously with nitrogen (upper picture, magnification × 150). The yeast type growth was obtained in a medium flushed with carbon dioxide (lower picture, magnification × 425). These photographs illustrate the fact, first recognized by Pasteur, that the type of growth and chemical activities of bacteria, yeasts and fungi are profoundly affected by the conditions of growth.*

ticular purpose, produced in pure culture under sterile conditions in scientific microbiological laboratories, and used in just the correct amount to permit standardization of the desired industrial processes. The yeast sold in the form of cakes or powder in grocery stores is made from factory grown yeast cultures. For the ease of distribution, the culture is compressed, and now commonly dehydrated, but despite the change in appearance the material in the cake or in the powder consists of living individual yeast cells. These have a typical yeast appearance when examined under the microscope and they start multiplying as soon as provided with water and the right kind of food. The methods used for the large-scale production of commercial yeast illustrate so well the impact of theoretical science on biological technology that it will prove worthwhile to consider some of their theoretical background.

Pasteur had shown that the chemical activities of yeast are profoundly affected by the supply of oxygen during fermentation and growth. In the absence of oxygen, the yield of alcohol from sugar is large, but the amount of yeast cells produced is small. In contrast, growth in the presence of an abundant supply of oxygen results in the production of very little alcohol, but of many yeast cells. The biochemical reason for this difference is that the production of alco-

A typical industrial plant, for the large scale production of yeast.

hol corresponds to an anaerobic transformation of the sugar which yields very little energy for the synthesis of yeast protoplasm, whereas availability of oxygen permits complete oxidation of the sugar and this releases much chemical energy for growth.

The technological practices of commercial yeast production are based on this theoretical knowledge of the biochemistry of fermentation and growth. During the industrial production of yeast, washed air is forced under pressure into the culture medium in order to favor complete oxidation of its sugar and other nutritional constituents. This permits efficient utilization of the nutrients and thus leads to maximum yields of cells. Needless to say the composition of the culture medium, its reaction, its temperature, and many other variables must be carefully controlled throughout growth of the yeast culture. Yeast production is therefore a technological process of great scientific complexity, in which microbiology, genetics, chemistry and physics all play essential parts. Even packaging presents interesting scientific problems. For while it is relatively easy to separate the yeast cells from the culture medium by high speed centrifugation, it is more difficult to maintain them in a highly active living state, especially while they are being desiccated.

During the past few decades, theoretical scientific research has led to entirely new industrial applications of yeast, for example to its use as a source of vitamin D. This new application follows from the fact that yeast cells contain relatively large amounts of ergosterol, a substance that can be converted into vitamin D by irradiation. In practice, the yeast cells which have been separated by centrifugation at the end of the growth period are exposed to the radiation from carbon arcs, and the ergosterol that they contain is thereby transformed into vitamin D. Through this simple operation the nutritional value of yeast can be greatly increased at low cost.

LIKE THE TRADITIONAL use of yeast in the making of wine, of beer, and of bread, the art of preparing cheese from milk through the activities of microorganisms is also very ancient. Empirically, the cheese maker has long known how to place milk under such conditions that the activities of lactic acid bacteria are favored, thus bringing about the conversion of milk sugar into lactic acid, with the consequent clotting of casein. Other steps in the process involve separating the casein clot from the whey and exposing it to conditions which have been found, empirically, to bring out the flavor and structure peculiar to each type of cheese — Emmental, Muenster, Camembert, Roquefort, etc. Microbiologists and biochemists have now worked out the scientific basis for all these empirical procedures and this knowledge permits a rational control of the various steps in cheese making. The transformation of milk into cheese has been shown to depend upon the activities of many types of microorganisms — bacteria, yeasts, molds — each one of them performing special

LEFT: *Roquefort cheese showing green veining produced by growth of the fungus which gives its flavor to the cheese.* RIGHT: *Swiss cheese showing holes produced by carbon dioxide arising from the fermentation of milk sugar by bacteria during ripening of the cheese. More generally, it can be said that each type of cheese owes its characteristic appearance and flavor to the chemical activities of the various kinds of microbes which transform the milk constituents during manufacture.*

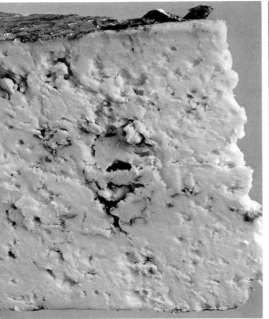

Root nodules produced by the proper strain of Rhizobium leguminosarum *on a 5–6 week old pea seedling* (Pisum sativum) *grown in white sand. The photograph was taken against dark soil, merely for good contrast.*

78

kinds of chemical changes which must occur in the right sequence. Production of lactic acid, digestion of casein, elaboration of aromatic constituents, all these complex reactions can go on in a satisfactory manner only if the cheese is allowed to ripen under the right conditions of temperature, humidity, atmospheric composition, etc. Today, cheese making is progressively becoming a scientific process which depends on the one hand upon the addition of the proper kind of microorganisms to the pasteurized milk, and on the other hand upon precise control of the physical environment during ripening. In brief, the aim is to duplicate scientifically in a controllable manner the conditions that had been empirically found favorable for the production of each particular type of cheese.

Microbes play a role in the preparation of many other foodstuffs — from the making of sauerkraut or silage to the fermentation of cacao or coffee beans. Other microbes are responsible for the biochemical changes that take place during the retting of flax, and the dehairing of hides used in the preparation of the finest kinds of leather. Many farming practices also have a microbiological basis, and among

Effect of inoculation with root nodule bacteria on the growth of soy bean. The two bunches of soy bean, uninoculated (left) and inoculated (right) were harvested from equal areas (137.5 sq. ft.).

*Three pioneers in
the discovery and
use of penicillin:* SIR ALEXANDER FLEMING
(1881–1955) born in Scotland

them none is more important than the use of leguminous plants to enrich the soil in nitrogen. As we shall again mention in the following chapter, there exist on the roots of these plants small nodules which harbor special kinds of bacteria that fix atmospheric nitrogen. In the past, the production of root nodules was left to nature, but now the various strains of nitrogen-fixing bacteria are grown artificially and used to inoculate legume plants under optimum conditions before seeding. Thus, even the farmer has come to depend on microbiological technology in order to increase the efficiency of crop production.

O NE OF THE MOST unexpected and spectacular applications of microorganisms to the welfare of man is their use in the treatment of disease. This particular aspect of microbiological technology is probably the one which has grown most rapidly during recent times but, despite common belief, it does not constitute an entirely new development. I had this point in mind when I mentioned ergot in the preceding chapter. Ergot, which is produced when the fungus *Claviceps purpurea* grows on rye grain, is a very powerful poison capable of

SIR HOWARD FLOREY
(1906 ——) born in Australia

ERNST CHAIN
(1898 ——) born in Germany

killing man and animals. But on the other hand, it is also true that this same poison is a very useful drug when administered at the proper time in the proper amount. One of its effects is to stimulate the contraction of involuntary muscle, in particular in the uterus, and for this reason physicians use it to facilitate labor in difficult cases of childbirth. Ergot was extensively used for this purpose during the 17th century as shown by many illustrations of the time.

One of the industries that has experienced the most dramatic gains during the past two decades is that concerned with the production of antimicrobial drugs — in other words of substances capable of attacking the microbial agents of disease in the body. Many of these drugs are produced by chemical synthesis, the sulfas for example. But the largest numbers of them are derived from certain kinds of fungi, from actinomycetes and from bacteria. The antimicrobial drugs of microbial origin are commonly called antibiotics and there is no doubt that their widespread use has caused a true revolution in the treatment of infectious diseases, indeed in the whole practice of medicine.

Penicillin is the most famous of the antibiotics not only because it was the first to have been discovered, chemically identified, and produced on an enormous industrial scale, but also because it is still today the most useful. The story of penicillin is worth telling because it illustrates the complex, roundabout way in which scientific discoveries are made. This story begins with the observation by Alexander Fleming in 1927 that a mold which had accidentally contaminated one of his nutrient agar plates completely inhibited the growth of staphylococcus on this plate. This was just a chance happening, an accident which would have remained meaningless to most persons, but Fleming had sufficient theoretical knowledge and scientific acumen to perceive the potential implications of the phenomenon that had come his way by chance.

"In science," Pasteur was wont to say, "chance favors only the prepared mind." Because Fleming's mind was "prepared," he proceeded to isolate the fungus which turned out to be a particular strain of *Penicillium*. He prepared from cultures of the fungus a filtrate which he found to be capable of inhibiting the growth of staphylococci as well as of many other bacteria. Fortunately the filtrate proved to be essentially non-toxic for animals. Because the active material came from a *Penicillium*, Fleming called it penicillin. Fur-

LEFT: *First batch of crystalline penicillin produced in the Oxford laboratory. It took two years to produce this small amount.* FACING PAGE: *(top) In the 1940's penicillin was produced on a large scale by growing the* Penicillium *in milk bottles. Contrast this primitive technique of production with the huge industrial plants of today (below).*

ther studies revealed that penicillin was chemically unstable, and for this reason difficult to prepare in a chemically pure state. After a few years Fleming had to abandon the work on penicillin because the problems involved in its handling went beyond his chemical skill.

With the advent of the Second World War, the need for antibacterial agents effective in the treatment of battle casualties became very acute. And this need stimulated a group of scientists in the Institute of Experimental Pathology at the University of Oxford in England to reinvestigate the potentialities of penicillin. One of the scientists was Howard Florey, a pathologist, and another Ernst Chain, a chemist. Together and in collaboration with several other laboratory scientists, they learned to stabilize, concentrate and purify penicillin, and this new chemical knowledge made it possible for them to obtain stable preparations of active material. As a result, penicillin could be tested in the treatment of bacterial infections of animals and of men.

Fundamental laboratory investigations and clinical tests established the immense practical value of penicillin, and thus encouraged the development of techniques for its large-scale production. Chemical and industrial engineers were called in to convert laboratory knowledge into practical industrial practices. And today, as a result of many years of efforts by microbiologists, chemists, physicians, geneticists, physicists, engineers, and many other types of specialists, penicillin is produced all over the world on a truly colossal scale, at a very low cost. No story could illustrate better the complex interplay between all aspects of science — from the simple observation of an individual person working alone in a small laboratory with very simple equipment, to the elaborate team work and the complicated apparatus required for development and for industrial production.

The production of vaccines constitutes another interesting and important application of domesticated microbes to the welfare of man. The practice of vaccination is based on the fact that resistance to certain microbial diseases can be greatly increased by injecting into the body some parts or products of the very microbes that cause these diseases. This practice is called vaccination and the increased

84

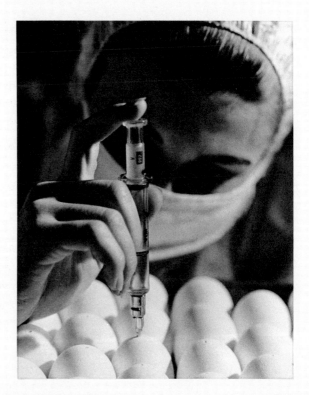

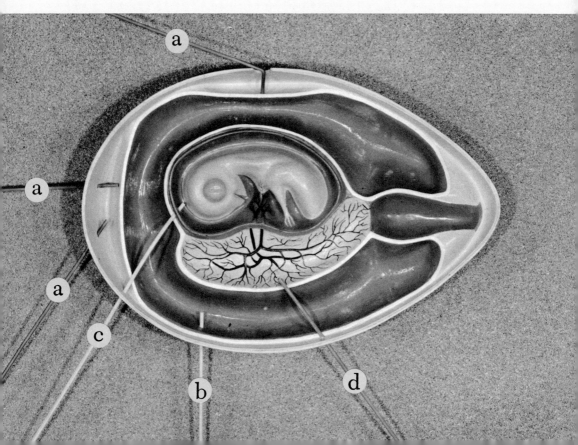

resistance which follows it results in general from the fact that injection of certain bacterial products elicits the production of protective antibodies. For example, most persons nowadays are vaccinated against diphtheria with toxoid derived from the diphtheria bacillus. The toxoid vaccine consists of diphtheria toxin which has been rendered innocuous by treatment with formaldehyde, in such a manner as to retain its power to elicit immunity through the production of protective antibodies. The Salk vaccine, which increases resistance to paralytic poliomyelitis, is another example in point. Fundamentally, this vaccine consists of a suspension of polioviruses killed and thus rendered innocuous, also by treatment with formaldehyde. In this case, the antibodies which are elicited by vaccination interfere with the multiplication of the virus in the susceptible tissue cells.

In the two examples which have just been mentioned the vaccine is made up of bacterial or viral constituents which have been killed by the proper treatment. Another way to vaccinate is to inject into the body bacteria or viruses which are still living, but have been modified by laboratory operations in such a manner that they are "attenuated" — avirulent is another word — which means that they are no longer able to produce severe disease. There are many such "attenuated" living vaccines which are highly effective. For example, the yellow fever vaccine is prepared by growing a modified form of the yellow fever virus in the developing chick embryo. Viruses of attenuated virulence can also be grown in vitro in other preparations of animal cells known as "tissue cultures". For example, a new type of polio vaccine made up of living virus no longer capable of causing disease is now being produced by growing this attenuated virus in cultures of cells derived from monkey kidneys. And a vaccine against the measles virus has been recently produced experimentally by a similar technique. The production of viruses in chick embryos or in tissue cultures was but a laboratory stunt a few years ago. Today, viruses can be grown on a large scale in industrial plants and this has permitted the development of a highly specialized industry of vaccine production which is rapidly growing in importance all over the world.

CLEARLY, THE ROLE of industrial technologists has been just as essential as those of laboratory scientists in bringing to perfection the highly complex and efficient techniques used in the modern factories where microorganisms are used for the production of yeast, enzymes, chemicals, antibiotics, vaccines, etc. And it is not because of negligence, nor for lack of time, that I have failed to describe the fascinating details of these industrial operations. The reason for not describing them is that equipment and techniques which appear so spectacularly modern and so efficient today will be outmoded within a few years and therefore do not have a lasting interest. As one surveys the history of technical procedures, it is striking to note that the practices based on empirical tradition last with hardly any change for many decades, indeed often for many centuries. In contrast, the techniques based on the findings of experimental science last but a few years and are unremittingly replaced by more efficient ones. This rapid turnover follows, of course, from the fact that experimental science constitutes an effective instrument for the discovery of new techniques and new procedures; as a result modern technology must continually evolve in order to incorporate the rapidly increasing knowledge. Just remember how the yeast industry has been influenced by biochemical understanding, and how the production of virus vaccines has been revolutionized by the development of tissue culture techniques. Among so many others that could be quoted to illustrate the impact of theoretical science on technological processes, I shall single out the role of genetics in the development of modern industrial microbiology.

As mentioned earlier, several of the most effective vaccines are made up of living bacteria or living viruses which have been modified by laboratory operations designed to decrease their virulence. This practice is based on the fact that bacteria and viruses, just like animals and plants, can undergo hereditary variations. In the words of genetics, populations of bacteria and viruses give rise to mutant forms which differ from the parent forms in certain characteristics, in virulence, for example. The study of these mutations is a very new science and only during the past few years has it become incorpo-

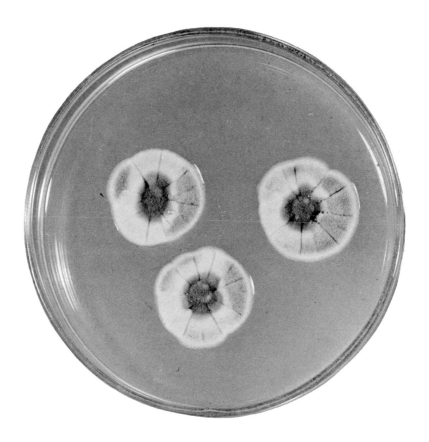

Culture SS-3 is a mutant of Penicillium chrysogenum *which gives very large yields of penicillin, and is used for this reason in industrial production.*

rated into textbooks; yet microbial genetics is already widely applied in many technological fields, for example in the selection of new bacterial and viral strains better suited for the production of vaccines.

Microbial genetics has also contributed greatly to the production of antimicrobial drugs, in particular to the production of penicillin by strains of *Penicillium*. When cultures of the mold are treated with the proper dose of ultraviolet radiation, their rates of mutation are much increased, and it becomes possible thereby to obtain many strains slightly different from the original. Some of the derivative strains thus obtained by irradiation have turned out to be much more potent penicillin producers than were those first isolated from nature, and for this reason they are now universally used in the industrial production of the drug. It is in large part because the yields of penicillin produced by the new mutant strains are so high that the cost of production of the drug has come down dramatically during recent years.

I N T H E L I G H T of all these facts, it should become easier to grasp what I have in mind when I use the word "domestication" as applied to microbial life. Several millenia ago man tamed wild plants and animals; then he selected certain breeds which he cultivated or raised on his farms or kept around his home. Likewise modern man has learned recently to manipulate microbial activities for his own ends, and even to change the hereditary characteristics of certain types of microorganisms. The examples that we have considered in the preceding pages are but a few among many others that could have been chosen to illustrate the range of human affairs which are affected by the domestication of microbial life. Man makes a valuable pigment of the ochre produced by bacteria from iron; he cultivates in factories the yeast blown by the wind on to his grapes; he takes the very molds that spoil his foodstuffs, and with them he converts milk into savory cheese or he manufactures drugs to combat diseases; even more extraordinary, he takes the most virulent infectious agents and he finds ways to modify them or to use their products in order to develop vaccines for increasing resistance to infection.

It seems to me that from many points of view, the domestication of microbial life has reached a level higher than that achieved in the domestication of animal and plant life. The animals and plants which are in common use today are still the same that primitive mankind had domesticated many thousands of years ago. Modern man has of course improved these animals and plants, but fundamentally he has added little to the achievements of his ancestors in this respect. In contrast, microbiologists continuously introduce into practical operations new species of microorganisms, and they now use the most advanced methods of genetics to produce more and more varieties of domesticated microbes. The shepherd still protects his flocks by using the dog which was empirically descended from the wolf, whereas the microbiologist produces at will countless mutants of fungi, bacteria and viruses to develop new products, drugs, and vaccines that can be used to enrich human life or to increase resistance against infection. Scientists began to work with microbes on a large scale less than a century ago, and yet they have already gone far towards applying all the resources of theoretical biology and chemistry to the domestication of microbial life.

CHAPTER FIVE

Biological Partnerships

I MENTIONED IN the second chapter that the mass of microbial protoplasm on earth can be reckoned to exceed some twenty times that of animal protoplasm. In one gram of garden soil there are many million bacteria, as well as immense numbers of actinomycetes, fungi, protozoa and helminths! Likewise, large numbers of many different species of microorganisms are always present in the various parts of our own body, in the bodies of all animals, and on the roots of all plants. It can be said in other words that microorganisms are a constant part of the natural environment of all living things. Moreover, as we shall see, they engage with them in all sorts of associations, and thus play a very important part in the concert of nature.

In view of the universal occurrence and diversity of microbial life under natural conditions, it becomes apparent that the picture we have drawn of it in the preceding chapters does not conform to reality, not because it is inexact in its details, but because it is incomplete. In the different topics that we have considered, each type of microbe has been discussed as a separate entity, as if it functioned separately and were more or less independent from the rest of the world. This analytical approach to the problems of microbiology was justified because we wanted to learn about the individual traits of each microbial type, its shape, its chemical activities, its ability to cause disease, and its potential usefulness in technology. For this purpose it was convenient to study each type of microbe by itself — in pure cultures as the microbiologist says. But microorganisms hardly ever exist in pure cultures under natural conditions. Except in the artificial environment created for them in the laboratory, they always live in association with other kinds of microorganisms, and also with all sorts of other living forms. To gain a better understanding of microbial life it is necessary, therefore, that we try to broaden the scope of our vision by moving from the artificial closed world of the laboratory to the open world. We must learn to observe the manifestations of microbial life as it really exists in nature at large.

The phenomena of microbial disease, discussed in the third chapter, correspond of course to one aspect of the interplay between microorganisms and other living things. But important as this aspect is from the practical point of view, especially as it regards man, it constitutes only a very small segment of the total spectrum of natural interrelationships. Observations in nature reveal that in fact, most microorganisms are capable of associating in many kinds of wonderfully interesting partnerships with other forms of life, usually reaching with them a state of subtle biological equilibrium favorable for the survival of all. Indeed, we shall see that these associations often extend the range of existence for many forms of life. As this statement is at odds with the prevailing view which identifies microbes with spoilage, destruction, and disease, I shall devote the present chapter to examples of helpful biological partnerships in which microorganisms are involved.

LICHENS DO NOT occupy much place in textbooks of biology; likewise they are sadly neglected by investigators and almost ignored by laymen. Yet these organisms are in many ways among the most successful living things, and also among the most beautiful and most interesting. They occur in many intriguing forms, with a wide range of colors, on the bark of trees, on rocks, and on waste lands. The so-called "reindeer moss" is in reality not a moss but a lichen which is

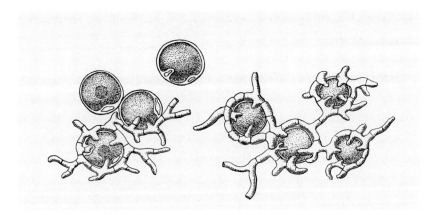

Diagram showing fungus mycelium around the symbiotic alga in a lichen.

widespread in our woods, and also covers immense areas of the Arctic land where hardly anything else can grow and where it constitutes the fundamental food of the reindeer — hence its name. In fact, it is a characteristic of lichens in general that they have the ability to become established and prosper under the most inimical conditions, even in places where life appears all but impossible. They are the first living things that develop and become visible on bare rocks, and they are abundant even in the most desolate places of the Antarctic.

What makes lichens so important for our discussion here is that they are made up of two very different microorganisms living in intimate association. In fact, the word symbiosis which means "life together" was introduced to denote the kind of biological association that lichens symbolize. Each lichen is the symbiotic summation of one species of alga and one species of fungus, the two organisms being so intimately interwoven that it is extremely difficult to separate them. Moreover, it is even more difficult to reconstitute the association once it has been broken, even though the fungus and the alga can be cultivated separately on adequate culture media.

There is no doubt that the alga and the fungus supplement each other nutritionally when they are associated in the form of a lichen. The alga contains chlorophyll and is therefore capable of manufacturing carbohydrates from the carbon dioxide of the air by photosynthesis. The fungus feeds on the carbohydrates, and in exchange supplies the alga with minerals and probably nitrogen that it extracts from the environment. Furthermore, the fungus acts as a reservoir of moisture. Although these nutritional interrelationships have not yet been worked out in detail, it is clear that they are of advantage to both members of the partnership. In any case, it is certain that lichens can multiply where nothing else will grow and can survive under conditions that seem incompatible with the survival of other living things. Lichens are among the examples I had in mind a while ago when stating that biological partnerships greatly extend the range of existence for many forms of life.

There exist numerous other situations in which microorganisms help the growth of plants by entering into biological association with them. The root nodules of beans, peas, alfalfa and other leguminous plants constitute the case most extensively studied. These nodules are produced by the response of the plant to the presence in the roots of special kinds of bacteria called *Rhizobium*. Although these bacteria become established on the rootlets and multiply in certain cells, normally they do not invade the rest of the plant. Leguminous plants can survive and indeed grow in the absence of *Rhizobium* bacteria, and therefore without forming root nodules, but then they usually grow less well, particularly in soils deficient in nitrogen. The reason is that root nodule bacteria have the ability to fix gaseous nitrogen from the air and convert it into organic nitrogenous compounds that can be utilized by the plant. In exchange, the plant supplies the bacteria with other nutrients necessary for their growth. The root nodules constitute therefore another example of nutritional partnership beneficial to both partners, a symbiosis between plants and bacteria.

Fungi also can enter into symbiosis with plants, for example with trees, heather, or orchids, forming with their roots associations which are called microrhizal. If orchid seeds are placed in a suitable environment, but without the proper fungus, either they do not germinate at all or else they fail to reach complete development. In contrast, the orchid plant develops fully if the seeds are inoculated

94

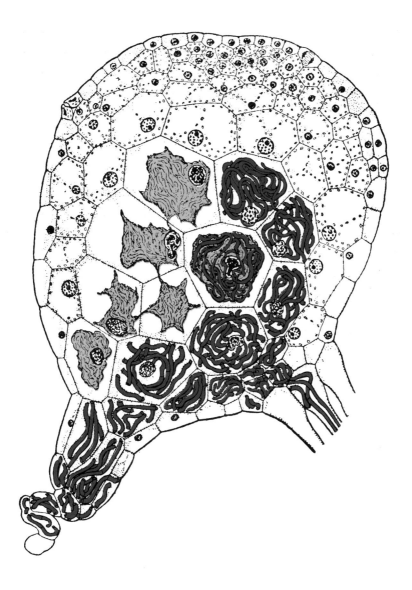

Section of a germinating seed of the orchid Odontoglossum *showing the intracellular coiling of the symbiotic fungus* Rhizoctonia lanuginosa *(dark color), as well as its destruction within certain cells (light color).*

at the proper time with the proper kind of fungus which grows in association with it and supplies it with several nutrients essential for growth. Fortunately, soil in which orchids naturally grow contain the necessary fungi so that the symbiotic association can take place spontaneously without the need of human intervention.

Symbiosis also occurs very frequently between microorganisms and animals. The common roach, for example, starves and fails to grow if deprived of the microorganisms with which it is always associated in nature! Termites owe their ability to destroy wood to the fact that they contain in their intestinal tract protozoa and bacteria capable of decomposing cellulose. These microorganisms convert the cellulose of wood into simpler compounds which in turn can be utilized by the termites.

The obvious contentment of the cow chewing its cud provides the best possible evidence of the beneficial effects resulting from the symbiosis between microorganisms and animals. "The cow does not

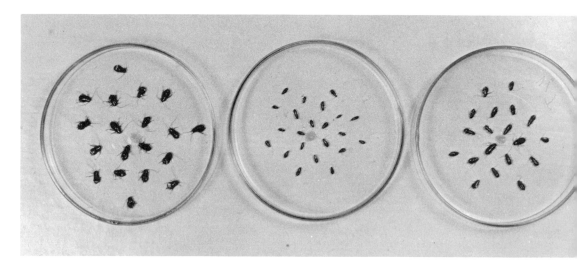

Roaches (Bratella germanica), *40 days old.* LEFT: *Normal roaches fed ground dog biscuit.* CENTER: *Roaches rendered free of their symbiotic microorganisms, and fed ground dog biscuit.* RIGHT: *Roaches treated like those in the center, but fed a diet enriched with 25 per cent yeast. Notice that the roaches in the center dish develop poorly because of absence of symbiont. Enrichment of the diet with yeast increases somewhat the growth of symbiont-free roaches.*

96

Fungus-growing ants. Whereas cultures of the fungi grown by gardener ants are rapidly overwhelmed by common microorganisms under usual laboratory conditions, these fungi thrive and remain uncontaminated in the ant garden. In this photograph the ant workers, 1.8 mm. long, are seen moving over the fungus garden and discarding unwanted material. The workers also deposit saliva and feces which favor the growth of the particular species of fungus which the ants cultivate.

eat much," an English boy is said to have written in his school essay, "but what it eats it eats twice so that it gets enough." What the schoolboy really meant by this cryptic statement is that in the cow as in other ruminants, the rough materials present in the forage must first be acted upon by a whole variety of microorganisms during rumination. The microbial flora of the rumen thus converts otherwise indigestible materials into soluble products which can then be assimilated and utilized as food.

Man is no exception to this rule of partnership with microbial

97

life. The billions of bacteria normally present in his intestine play a role as yet ill-defined, but certainly important, because some of them manufacture vitamins and other nutrients essential for his well-being. It is thanks to the activity of the microbes in his gut that man has so long remained independent of the chemical industry for his requirements in certain vitamins.

IN ALL THE examples considered so far, the symbiotic relationship has a nutritional basis. This particular aspect of the symbiosis problem has been the most extensively studied, chiefly because nutrition is a factor of such obvious importance for survival and for growth. It is certain, however, that symbiosis often results in other types of biological effects even more interesting. Lichens, for exam-

---

RIGHT: *"British soldier" lichen. Like other lichens, this one is the composite expression of an alga and a fungus. These two microorganisms are shown here growing separately in pure culture: the alga in a test tube, and the fungus in a Petri dish. It is only when the alga and the fungus grow in symbiotic association that they produce the complex and beautiful structures and pigments found in the lichen.*
BELOW: *This drawing shows a broken fragment of lichen body with both the fungal (colorless) and the algal (black) cells. Only if both constituents are living and associated can the fragment propagate into new lichen growth.*

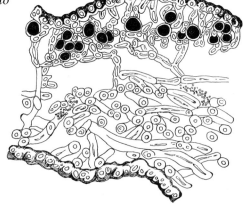

ple, exhibit complex morphological structures and synthesize peculiar organic acids and pigments that neither one of their constituents, alga nor fungus, can produce alone. Looking at the delicately shaped and bright red structures of the common lichen known as "British soldier," for example, it is difficult to believe that such a startling appearance can result from the association of a microscopic alga and a microscopic fungus. Nor would it have been possible to predict from the known characters of its two components that the lichen could synthesize the peculiar chemical substances that it produces, or exhibit such great ability to survive heat, cold, or dryness. In other words, the characteristics of the lichen are much more than the sum of the characteristics of its fungal and algal components.

The association of the leguminous plants with *Rhizobium* pro-

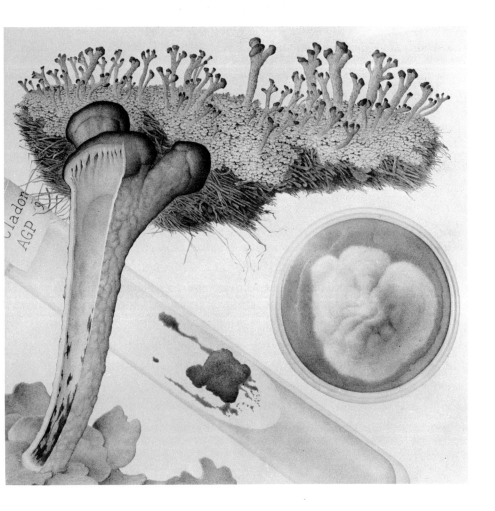

vides another startling illustration of the creative effect of symbiosis. The root nodules contain a red pigment which is almost identical with the hemoglobin of red blood cells! This form of hemoglobin cannot be produced by the bacterium or by the plant alone, nor for that matter is it known to occur anywhere else in the plant world. It seems to be formed only in the plant cells which harbor the *Rhizobium*.

Thus, it is clear that symbiosis is more than an additive association; it is a creative force which can result in the production of unpredictable new structures, functions and properties. In terms of the total economy of nature, the creative associations in which microbes are involved are probably far more important than are the diseases that they cause, or than the practical uses that man makes of them. Indeed, the entirely new creative processes that these associations represent give to the phenomenon of symbiosis a significance which transcends analytical biology and reaches into the very philosophy of life.

Before concluding these essays, I should like to express some of my personal philosophy concerning a larger aspect of the problem of interrelationships between living things. To introduce this topic, I have used on purpose the expression "personal philosophy" because, as will appear from what follows, I intend to go beyond objective knowledge and make bold to express feelings inspired in me by certain selected facts. In other words, I shall now behave not only as an experimental scientist, but also as a human being reacting to some aspects of science which have impressed him emotionally.

The lichens that we discussed a while ago might serve as a symbol of what I have in mind. The biologists who study them usually emphasize that the symbiotic association between fungus and alga results in a greater ability to obtain food from unfavorable localities and to resist all sorts of inimical influences. Important as these aspects of symbiosis certainly are, even more important is the fact that lichens derive from their composite nature a strange beauty possessed by neither the alga nor the fungus alone. From the human

LEFT: Abutilon striatum *var.* Thompsonii—*sold in florist shops under the name flowering maple — owes its ornamental value to the interesting patterns of variegation in the leaves. These patterns are produced by infection with a mosaic type of virus which interferes with deposition of chlorophyll, but does not endanger the life of the plant.* Abutilon *can be grown from seed, free of virus, but its leaves are then uniformly green, and devoid of ornamental value.* RIGHT: *The white veins in the pale veined honeysuckle also result from a mild virus infection.*

point of view at least, the partnership between the two organisms has effects which transcend obvious predictable biological utility and which add something unexpected to the interest and richness of life.

Equally remarkable is the fact that infection with certain viruses has been shown to enhance the beauty or at least the decorative value of certain plants. For example, *Abutilon striatum* var. *Tompsonii*, known in florist shops as flowering maple, owes its popularity to the fact that its leaves exhibit interesting patterns of variegations. The point of interest here is that these variegations are caused by a virus which interferes with the deposition of chlorophyll in certain parts of the leaves. The pale veined honeysuckle and the Wedgwood iris also exhibit variegations in their leaves caused by other types of viruses. In certain plants the viral infection expresses itself by variegations which occur not so much in the leaves, as in the petals of the flower — for instance in the petals of the tulip, the wallflower, the larkspur, the pansy, and the camellia.

101

In all these cases — which are but a few among so many other examples that could have been selected—the infected plant and the virus exist in a kind of biological equilibrium, with the result that both survive and that the plant acquires a decorative value that it does not have in the uninfected state. The case of the tulip is especially interesting in this regard, and for this reason I feel justified in presenting here some details of its history.

The tulip was introduced from Turkey into Europe for the first time in 1555. Within a very few years, interest in the flower became a craze as well as a big business, especially in Holland. The production and sale of new varieties of tulip soon developed into a speculative orgy which affected all social groups. This most incredible of financial booms reached its peak in Holland between 1634 and 1637, and has found its place in history under the name "tulipomania." From many paintings and illustrations published during the 17th, 18th and 19th centuries, we know the appearance of the varieties of tulips which achieved the greatest fame in the past. And these illustrations reveal that the famous ancient tulips differ greatly from those commonly seen at present. Their blossoms are variegated, exhibiting all sorts of unusual patterns of the petals, whereas the modern tulips are usually of solid uniform colors.

The famous tulips of the past were characterized by distinctive patterns of flower pigmentation It is now known that these patterns were the result of a mild infection with a virus which interfered with deposition of the pigment in the petals. Many varieties of tulips have been maintained for several centuries, in a state of equilibrium with the virus, by bulb propagation.
RIGHT: *Illustration of variegated tulip from an 18th century garden book.*
FAR RIGHT: *Tulips grown from seed and free of virus produce petals of uniform color. Inoculation in the laboratory with the proper strain of virus gives progressive degrees of variegation depending upon the extent of viral multiplication.*

It has been known since 1927 that the variegations, the distinctive floral patterns of the ancient varieties of tulips, are the results not of genetic mutation, but of a viral infection. The virus is present in the plant, and interferes with the deposition of pigment in certain areas of the petals, thus determining the color pattern of the flower. To many tulip lovers the variegated forms look more beautiful and more interesting than do the ordinary uninfected flowers; they have more character. It must be admitted that the viral infection prevents the tulips from reaching their maximum potential size, or from producing the maximum numbers of bulbs. But size is not a very significant criterion of success — biological or otherwise. In fact, some of the tulips which are variegated because they are infected have been cherished and cultivated all over the world, for hundreds of years. For example, the *Zomerschoon* tulip has been a favorite ever since it was introduced into Europe in the 16th century. Even though consistently virus infected, it has flourished in countless gardens and given joy to countless hearts.

There is perhaps a lesson, or at least a hope, to be derived from contemplating the many types of effects that microbial life can exert on living things. In some cases, it is true, the presence of microbes spells disease, or even death. But more often a state of mutual toler-

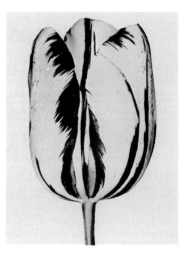

ance becomes established between the microorganism and its host. The result is then a type of association which can be useful, or at least which gives rise to interesting results. The ultimate outcome may be more efficient utilization of food as occurs in the rumen of the cow or through the fixation of nitrogen in the root nodules of legume plants. It may be an increase in vigor and in adaptibility as exemplified by the lichens. It may be greater beauty and interest as in the variegated tulips or other ornamental plants. Is it too far fetched to point out that analogous consequences usually result from associations among people of different origins, and of different creeds? Admittedly, there is some unforeseeable danger in these associations, but if they occur under the proper circumstances and are well managed, they usually bring unexpected rewards and enrich the life of all.

I WISH IT WERE possible to summarize in a few words the facts and principles discussed in these lectures, with their bearing on theoretical science and their applications to human life. But the territory that we have surveyed is so varied and wide that it would be impossible to give an adequate account of it in a simplified sketch. Fortunately, we have on several occasions during our journey reached high points which have permitted us to link the field of microbiology with other areas of science and especially with general biology. As we studied microorganisms from the point of view of their shape and structure, their chemical activities, and the mechanisms through which they transfer hereditary characteristics to their progeny, it became clear that fundamentally all microorganisms are in essence constructed like other living things, only smaller. The biophysical and biochemical unity of life is certainly one of the largest contributions of modern science to philosophical thought. And then, we have come to realize that like other forms of life, microorganisms never exist as isolated entities in nature, and function best when operating together in integrated biological complexes. Thus, unexpectedly, the study of microbial life brings support to moral law by showing that the evolution of biological relationships is toward tolerance and mutual aid.

104

CHAPTER SIX

Science as a Way of Life

In the discussions that followed the lectures on which the preceding account is based, I was asked several questions which had no direct bearing on the subject matter of microbiology, but which dealt in a general manner with science as a way of life. Some of these questions were so far removed from my professional activities and competence that I might have been expected to ignore them. Yet I tried to answer them because they revealed among the listeners a deep concern with the larger significance of the scientific process, and with some of the very perplexing problems that the scientist faces as a human being.

I was asked for example: "Is the pursuit of science compatible with active interest in other cultural subjects such as art, literature, music, or history?" "Can science give answers to the questions that most deeply preoccupy thoughtful human beings?" And finally "Would you still choose to become a scientist if you were to start your life all over again?" I shall present here almost verbatim my answers to these questions. However, I wish to make clear at the outset that the answers should not be construed as expressing the consensus of the commonwealth of Science. They represent only an attitude developed out of personal experience.

I shall preface my remarks by acknowledging that, for those who take it seriously, a life in science is very demanding indeed. Few are the evenings or the holidays during which I do not find it necessary to devote a good deal of my time to the study or the preparation of scientific material. This necessity has compelled me of course to neglect some other occupations and amusements which I might have enjoyed otherwise. But in reality, this neglect has never taken the form of real sacrifice. Rather it has involved choices among several types of activities that I could have pursued. What is certain is that it has never made me feel that I was divorcing myself from normal human pursuits.

The English novelist C. P. Snow, who started his career as a scientist, has recently popularized the theme that our society is suffering from a split between the "two cultures," that is, between science and the humanities. As I have discussed at some length in my recent book *The Dreams of Reason*, I see no real basis for believing that the problem symbolized by the expression "The Two Cultures" is very different today from what it has been in the past.

Every sensible man now recognizes that science is as much a part of culture as are the subjects referred to as humanities. In the modern world, no one can claim to be cultured who does not have some understanding of scientific facts and principles. Moreover, it is certain that the increasing importance of science in public affairs is compelling scientists to become deeply involved in all forms of human activities. In a curious but very real way, scientific technology has established a much-travelled bridge between the world of cold facts and the throbbing life of the man of flesh and bone.

Despite common belief, the interplay between science and the rest of society is not a new phenomenon. True enough, there is a tendency at present to regard science as an activity peculiar to our times, and to assume that it began acquiring great social importance and captivating public concern only after the discovery of the miracle drugs, the explosion of the atomic bomb, and the excitement caused by sputnik and space exploration. In reality, however, public interest in science has deeper and far more interesting origins. During the

106

second half of the 18th century and throughout the 19th century, the general educated public of Europe and America was keenly interested in theoretical science and well aware of its practical implications. The success of the Christmas lectures throughout the 19th century in London reflected an attitude which was fairly common in most countries of Western civilization, as illustrated by the fact that scientific lectures and demonstrations attracted everywhere large and fashionable audiences. Books on "natural philosophy," as science was then called, were found in every well appointed private library and were widely read and discussed among non-specialists.

I have introduced here the old fashioned expression "natural philosophy," because it corresponds to an attitude toward science that deserves to be cultivated more than ever today. There would be little chance, however, of maintaining the noble tradition of natural philosophy if it were true that the world of learning is on the way to dividing itself into separate uncommunicating camps, corresponding to the two cultures of C. P. Snow. Fortunately, there is no reason to believe that scientific studies are incompatible with active interest in other areas of human endeavour. Many of the greatest scientists cultivate philosophy, play music, draw or paint, write poetry, and participate actively in local or world politics. It is true of course that other scientists become narrow specialists; but I have seen no evidence that this makes them more competent or more productive in their field of specialization. Scientists who assert that scientific knowledge is the only form of culture worth cultivating might profit from reading what Charles Darwin wrote in his autobiography.

"For many years," Darwin wrote, "I cannot endure to read a line of poetry. I have tried lately to read Shakespeare, and found it so unendurably dull that it nauseated me. I have also almost lost my tastes for pictures and music ... My mind seems to have become a kind of machine for grinding general laws out of large collections of facts. But why this should have caused the atrophy of that part of the brain alone on which the higher tastes depend I cannot conceive. A man with a mind more highly organized or better constituted than mine would not I suppose have suffered; and if I had to live my life again

I would have made a rule to read some poetry and listen to some music at least once every week; for perhaps the parts of my brain now atrophied could thus have been kept active through use. The loss of these tastes is a loss of happiness, and may possibly be injurious to the intellect, and more probably to the moral character, by enfeebling the emotional part of our nature."

Darwin's remarks point to one aspect of scientific life which caused much concern to some of my listeners and made them question the wisdom of devoting one's life to science. Obviously, some of the richest human values have remained almost completely outside the fold of orthodox science. Certainly the arts, and classical philosophy seem at first sight to come much closer than does science to many of the problems of existence that have always haunted mankind. Again speaking for myself, I shall confess that time and time again I too have felt some discouragement from realizing that science does not provide clearcut answers to the questions that preoccupy us most deeply: the place of man in the cosmos, and the meaning of life. Often also, I have felt the urge to turn to some other form of activity, artistic perhaps, or philosophical, that would liberate me from the exacting discipline of the scientific method and allow an uninhibited and more total expression of my personality. But on the other hand, there are large compensations in scientific pursuits, and taken together they satisfy me and give me confidence that I have made a good choice for my life.

First, science provides a feeling of intellectual and emotional security because, however limited the philosophical significance of its achievements, these have a lasting value, and constitute evidence that mankind is progressing. I might be permitted to quote here the words of the very great microbiologist, Louis Pasteur, who cannot be accused of having been a coldhearted scientist because in fact he repeatedly acknowledged in public that the feelings of the heart were for him as important as the acquisition of knowledge. "The experimental method," Pasteur wrote, "rarely leads astray and then only those who do not use it well . . . The charm of our studies, the enchantment of science, is that everywhere and always we can give the

108

Aristotle, in his Metaphysics, *expressed beautifully the spirit of scientific research: "The search for Truth is in one way hard and in another easy. For it is evident that no one can master it fully nor miss it wholly. But each adds a little to our knowledge of Nature, and from all the facts assembled there arises a certain grandeur." This quotation (Met. A: 993.A.30) is inscribed in Greek on the building of the National Academy of Sciences in Washington. The text shown above is from the earliest manuscript of the* Metaphysics *known, written in the tenth century and now in the Bibliothèque Nationale in Paris.*

justification of our principles and the proof of our discoveries." Happy are those who can experience "the serene peace of laboratories and libraries!"

Science, it is true, has not yet given a final answer to the questions that most preoccupy mankind, but as a scientist I am proud of taking part in an exciting and extraordinary adventure that began long before me, and that will continue long after me. Again in Pasteur's words, "Laboratories . . . are the temple of the future. There it is that

109

humanity grows, becomes stronger and better. There it learns to read the works of nature, symbols of progress and of universal harmony; whereas the works of man are too often those of fanaticism and destruction."

As a conclusion the best I can do, it seems to me, is to answer the questions of my readers by a statement of my faith.

I believe that, by the exercise of science as well as of other intellectual pursuits, mankind grows continuously into some higher form and that in some mysterious way it is in the process of transcending itself. While my own contribution to this upward trend will of course be very small, it has an immense value nevertheless, because it becomes part of a spiritual structure that is endlessly emerging from amorphous matter. Science is not only an effort to gather knowledge and develop techniques for achieving mastery over nature. As Aristotle wrote two thousand years ago in his *Ethics*, science is above all the search for understanding. Aristotle's words still convey today the very spirit of the scientific way of life. While it may never be possible to reach absolute truth, nevertheless each one of us adds a small stone to the structure of knowledge, and from all these efforts there emerges a certain grandeur.

ACKNOWLEDGMENTS

The photographs and illustrations have been provided by courtesy of the individuals and organizations listed below, and are reproduced with their permission.

4   Rijksmuseum, Amsterdam, Netherlands

5   Mauritshuis, Amsterdam, Netherlands

6   Rijksmuseum, Amsterdam, Netherlands

7   Lambert-Hudnut Division of Warner-Lambert Pharmaceutical Co., St. Louis, Missouri

13 Upper left and right: Robinow, C.F., University of Western Ontario, London, Canada
    Lower right: Robinow, C.F.
    Lower left: Wild Heerbrugg, Ltd., Heerbrugg, Switzerland

14 Johnson, F.H., Zworykin, N. and Warren, G., J. Bact., 1943, **46**, 167

15 Williams, Marion A., J. Bact., 1961, **81**, 195

16 Top and lower right: Robinow, C.F., University of Western Ontario, London, Canada
    Lower left: Simpson, Charles F., and White, F.H., J. of Infec. Dis., 1961, **109**, 243

17 Anderson, T.F., Wollman, E.L., and Jacob, F., Ann. Inst. Pasteur, 1957, **93**, 450

18 Culture obtained from William Bridge Cooke, Robert A. Taft Sanitary Engineering Center, Cincinnati, Ohio. Photo by Illustration Service, The Rockefeller Institute, New York

19 From the film "Life of the Molds," Pfizer and Company, New York

21 Houwink, A.L., Biochimica et Biophysica Acta, 1953, **10**, 360

24 Upper left: Hart, R.G., Proc. National Academy U.S., 1955, **41**, 261
    Upper right: Steere, R.L. and Schaffer, F.L., Biochimica et Biophysica Acta, 1958, **28**, 241
    Lower right: Stanley, W.M., Am. J. Botany, 1937, **24**, 59

25 Steere, R.L. and Schaffer, F.L., Biochimica et Biophysica Acta, 1958, **28**, 241

26 Jesaitis M.A. and Hutton, J.J., Bact. Proc. 1962, 144. Photograph by M.A. Jesaitis and S. Dales.

27 Horne, R.W., J. Mol. Bio., 1959, **1**, 281

32 Pasteur Museum, Pasteur Institute, Paris, France

33 Pasteur Museum, Pasteur Institute, Paris, France

35 Pasteur Museum, Pasteur Institute, Paris, France

36 Pasteur Museum, Pasteur Institute, Paris, France

39 Pasteur Museum, Pasteur Institute, Paris, France

40 Pasteur Museum, Pasteur Institute, Paris, France

42 Pasteur Museum, Pasteur Institute, Paris, France

45 Photo by Illustration Service, The Rockefeller Institute, New York

47 Pramer, David, Rutgers University, New Brunswick, New Jersey and Stoll, Norman, The Rockefeller Institute, New York

49 Photo by Illustration Service, The Rockefeller Institute, New York

53 Godlee, R.J., "Lord Lister," Macmillan & Co., London, 1918

55 Bettmann Archive, Inc., New York

57 Robert Koch Institute, Berlin, Germany

59 Robert Koch Institute, Berlin, Germany

60 Robert Koch Institute, Berlin, Germany

63 Hirsch, James G., The Rockefeller Institute, New York

64 Pijper, Adrianus, Pretoria, South Africa

65 Pfizer and Company, New York

67 Smith, Kline and French, Ars Medica Collection, Philadelphia Museum of Art, Philadelphia, Pa.

69 Anderson, T.F., Wollman, E.L., and Jacob, F., Anns. Inst. Pasteur, 1957, 93, 450

73 Top: Fleischmann Yeast Company, New York
    Bottom: Nickerson, Walter, Sci. Am., 1960, Feb., 138

74 Nickerson, Walter, and Bartnicki-Garcia, A., Rutgers University, New Brunswick, New Jersey

75 Fleischmann Yeast Company, New York

77 Roquefort Association, Inc., New York. Switzerland Cheese Association, Inc., New York

78 Allen, O.N., University of Wisconsin, Madison, Wisconsin

79 Wilson, Perry, University of Wisconsin, Madison, Wisconsin

80, 81 Vogue Magazine, New York (photographs of Fleming and Florey)
    Photograph of Chain from the film "The Story of Penicillin," Imperial Chemical Industries, England

82 Imperial Chemical Industries, England

83 Top: Wyeth Laboratories, Philadelphia, Pennsylvania
    Bottom: Merck & Co., Rahway, New Jersey

85 Lederle Laboratories, Pearl River, New York

88 Squibb Institute for Medical Research, New Brunswick, New Jersey

93 Hale, Mason, "Lichen Handbook," Smithsonian Institution, Washington, D.C., 1961

95 Caullery, Maurice, "Parisitism & Symbiosis," Sidgwick & Jackson Ltd., London, 1952

96 Brooks, Marion A., University of Minnesota

97 Neal Weber, Swarthmore College, Swarthmore, Pennsylvania

98 Lamb, I. Mackenzie, Sci. Am., 1959, Oct., 145

99 Lamb, I. Mackenzie, Sci. Am., 1959, Oct., 146

102, 103 Van Slogteren, E. Onderzoekingen over virus-zeikten in bloembolgewassen, II, Tulpen I, May, 1941

109 Bibliothèque Nationale, Paris, France

Colophon illustration of microscope from Pasteur Museum, Pasteur Institute, Paris, France

*The microscope shown here and adapted for
the binding design was used by Pasteur for much of his
research. The text type is Caledonia, designed originally
for Linotype by W. A. Dwiggins and here composed directly
on film by Fotosetter at Westcott & Thomson. Printed on
S-N text by The Meriden Gravure Company in offset lithog-
raphy and duotone, with binding by Russell-Rutter Company.
The book was designed by Reynard Biemiller.*